MAYOMBE

Translated from the Portuguese by
Michael Wolfers

Heinemann

Heinemann Educational Publishers
A Division of Heinemann Publishers (Oxford) Ltd
Halley Court, Jordan Hill, Oxford OX2 8EJ

Heinemann: A Division of Reed Publishing (USA) Inc.
361 Hanover Street, Portsmouth, NH 03801–3912, USA

Heinemann Educational Books (Nigeria) Ltd
PMB 5205, Ibadan

Heinemann Educational Botswana Publishers (Pty) Ltd
PO Box 10103, Village Post Office, Gaborone, Botswana

FLORENCE PRAGUE PARIS MADRID
ATHENS MELBOURNE JOHANNESBURG
AUCKLAND SINGAPORE TOKYO
CHICAGO SÃO PAULO

© Artur Pestana (Pepetela) – Edicoes 70, 1980
First published in African Writers Series in 1983

First published in English by Heinemann Educational Publishers in this
edition in 1996

Translation © Michael Wolfers

Series Editor: Abdulrazak Gurnah

The right of Artur Pestana (Pepetela) to be identified as the author of this
work has been asserted by him in accordance with the Copyright,
Designs and Patents Act 1988.

British Library Cataloguing in Publication Data
A catalogue record for this book is available from the British Library.

AFRICAN WRITERS SERIES and CARIBBEAN WRITERS SERIES and
their accompanying logos are trademarks in the United States of America
of Heinemann: A Division of Reed Publishing (USA) Inc.

ISBN 0 435 905 953

Cover design by Touchpaper
Cover illustration by Nick Higgins
Author photograph by Bernd Böhner

Photoset by CentraCet Limited, Cambridge
Printed and bound in Great Britain
by Cox & Wyman Ltd, Reading, Berks

96 97 98 99 8 7 6 5 4 3 2 1

To the guerrillas of Mayombe,
    who dared challenge the gods
        by opening a path through the dark forest,
I am going to relate the tale of Ogun,
                    the African Prometheus.

Translator's Preface

This novel is set in the Mayombe forest of Angola's enclave province of Cabinda, among a group of guerrilla fighters for the People's Movement for the Liberation of Angola (MPLA) in the early 1970s, and at Dolisie in the neighbouring Congo Republic, where MPLA had a rear-base and school. MPLA had launched the armed struggle for national liberation after an unsuccessful attack, at dawn on 4 February 1961, on the prisons in Luanda, where nationalists were held by the International Police for the Defence of the State (PIDE) of colonial Portugal. The MPLA's action in Luanda was followed in March 1961 by a rising in the north of Angola led by the Union of the Peoples of Angola (UPA), a tribally based grouping that had grown out of a northern peoples' union.

Pepetela, who wrote the book in 1971, served with the guerrillas in Cabinda and discusses frankly the tensions within a national liberation movement that included in its ranks people from all the ethnic groups in Angola, such as Kikongo in the north, Kimbundu in the centre and Umbundu in the south, and in the context of Cabinda where Fiote is one of several vernacular languages. The book was not published during the liberation struggle, but several years after the People's Republic of Angola won independence in November 1975 under MPLA leadership. The publication in its original Portuguese version in Luanda and Lisbon in 1980 was at the express wish of Angola's first president, Agostinho Neto, who had died in September 1979. It is believed that he felt the open debate on the dangers of tribalism and racism was worth pursuing in the wider context of independent Africa.

Michael Wolfers
London, 1982

CHAPTER 1

Mission

The river Lombe was shining in the thick undergrowth. He had crossed it a score of times. Theory, the teacher, had slipped on a stone and deeply gashed his knee. The Commander had told Theory to return to Base with a guerrilla escort. Pulling a face, the teacher had answered:

'There are sixteen of us. We'll be left with fourteen.'

Simple mathematics to settle the matter: it was difficult to raise enough manpower. Reluctantly, the Commander gave the order to advance. From time to time he went up to Theory, who was travelling at the rear, to ask how he was feeling. The teacher hid the pain. And he smiled listlessly.

When the time came to make camp, some of the fighters went in search of dry firewood, while the Command had a meeting. The medic, Pangu-Akitina, put a dressing on the teacher's injury. The knee was very swollen, and he could walk only with great effort.

In groups of four, they prepared dinner: rice and corned beef. They finished eating at six in the evening, when the sun had already gone down and night covered Mayombe. The gigantic trees, from which hung creepers as thick as cables, were dancing in the shadows with the flicker of the flames. Only the smoke could escape from Mayombe and climb up between the leaves and the lianas to spread rapidly in space, like the water spilled by a small waterfall and spreading over a lake.

I, THE NARRATOR, AM THEORY.

I was born in Gabela, in coffee country. From the land I received the dark colour of coffee, from my mother's side, mixed with off-white from my father, a Portuguese trader. I carry in me the irreconcilable and that is my driving force. In a Universe of yes or no, white or black, I represent the

1

maybe. Maybe says no for someone who wants to hear yes and means yes for someone who wants to hear no. Is it my fault if men insist on purity and reject compounds? Am I the one who must turn me into a yes or a no? Or must men accept the maybe? In the face of this essential problem, people are divided in my view into two categories: Manichaeans and the rest. It is worth explaining that the rest are rare; the World generally is Manichaean.

The Political Commissar, tall and thin like Theory, approached him.

'Command think that you should go back or wait for us here. Within three days we'll be back again. Someone will stay with you. Or you could try to make your way to Base slowly. It depends on your condition.'

The teacher unhesitatingly answered:

'I think that would be a mistake. I can still walk. We are short of people, two guerrillas fewer would make a big difference. The plan would be messed up.'

'Few, but perhaps enough.'

'May I speak to Command?'

'I'll go and see.'

The Commissar went back to the Commander and Operations Chief. After a few moments he beckoned to Theory. The teacher stood up and a sharp pain shot through his knee and up to his belly. He felt that he could not go on much longer. The relative darkness hid his features and no-one noticed the grimace. He tried to walk normally as he approached the three seniors.

Commander Fearless stared at him fixedly, as the teacher sat down with a silent cry of agony to hide the unbearable pain. I am stuck, he thought.

'It's no use acting so strong,' Fearless said. 'It's obvious that you're all in, even if you try to hide it. I don't see the harm in admitting that you cannot go on. You would be a dead-weight on us.'

Theory gave a shrug of annoyance.

'I know how I feel. I say that I can go on. I've had treatment and tomorrow I'll be better. Clearly there is nothing broken, it's only a slight graze. Even the risk of infection is past.'

'Suppose we were to meet the enemy tomorrow,' the Commissar said, 'and had to make a rapid withdrawal, you wouldn't be able to run.'

'Would you like me to run here and now to prove that I can?'

'I'm opposed to your taking part,' the Commissar reiterated. 'There's no point in insisting.'

Stretched out on a groundsheet, the Operations Chief was studying the tree shadows. He heard the talk of the others and was thinking of the rain that was about to fall and of his warm house in Dolisie, with his wife at his side.

'It is clear that the Commissar has objective reason on his side,' said the Commander. 'But I understand comrade Theory ... For my part, if he thinks he can go on, I will not stand in the way. But objectively speaking the Commissar is right ...'

'And subjectively?' the Commissar asked.

'Subjectively ... who knows? Sometimes a man needs to suffer, needs to know that he is suffering and needs to overcome that suffering. For what purpose, why? Sometimes, for no reason. Sometimes, for many reasons that he does not know, cannot or will not explain. Theory knows and could explain. But he does not wish to, and I think he's right about that.'

'The difficulty is that we are talking about a war operation and not an outing. On an outing, a chap can act against all reason, just because he feels like turning left rather than right. In war he forfeits this choice, it puts others' lives at risk ...'

'In this instance? No, here he's risking only his own, and even so ... I know that if we have to take to our heels, Theory will look like a champion. He hasn't got a broken leg, so let's not exaggerate. The medic says that the thing's not serious, just painful. It will soon go. Why not give him a chance?'

'A chance for what? That's what I don't understand!'

'Obviously not! A chance ... don't know! He's the man who knows. But he certainly won't want to say, and I agree with him. Comrade Theory has two possibilities: to go or not to go. He chose the former. Perhaps wrongly, perhaps without much thought, but he chose. And he is not a man to go back on his choice. Whether it's obstinacy or not, he's the only one who knows. What I know is that obstinate men usually stay like that to the last, especially when there is danger. If he wants to crack his head, if he has chosen to crack his head, we must give him the freedom to crack his head.'

'That is liberalism!'

'There you go with your jargon! It may be liberalism. But I am not the Political Commissar. It's your task to politicize us and to defend the correct political line. I can be liberalistic now and then, because I have you as my guardian angel always to guide me.'

The Commissar smiled. Though the Commander was ten years older than he, the former was now behaving childishly to divert the argument. It was clear that Fearless already had some idea in his head.

'And what about you, comrade Operations Chief, what do you think?' the Commander asked.

'I think you're right,' he answered abstractedly.

'So, I'm in the minority,' the Commissar said. 'It is your responsibility, Commander. I hope nothing happens.'

'One responsibility more or less!' Fearless said.

'Nothing will happen,' Theory riposted, without knowing whether to feel pleased or not: he did not ask himself.

The Operations Chief had fallen asleep. Theory went to lie down. Soon they would wake to the light dew that would begin by dampening the tree canopy and start to fall from the leaves only when it had already stopped raining. Such is Mayombe, with a power to delay nature's will.

The teacher scarcely slept. His soaked leg was atrociously painful. Why had he insisted? His participation would make no difference. He knew that he was not an outstanding guerrilla, nor even a good guerrilla. But he had insisted. It was his secret. In just the same way he had forced on Command the obligation to give him guard duty like the other guerrillas, although his post as Base teacher exempted him from this. Theory was of mixed blood and now no-one seemed to notice this about him. It was his secret. A sad secret, which the Commissar had not perceived, to which the Operations Chief had paid no attention. Only Fearless, a veteran of war and of men, had guessed.

Fearless, a guerrilla fighter with Henda. Earlier he had called himself Sphinx, no-one knew why. When he was promoted to Section Chief, the guerrillas gave him the name Fearless, because he had single-handedly resisted an enemy unit attacking a forward position, and allowed time for the Base to be evacuated without casualties. It was one of many operations in which he had mocked the enemy, throwing bullets, taunts and curses at them.

Theory sensed that the Commander too had a secret. Like each of the rest of them. And it was the secret in each of them that made them fight, often for reasons far from the stated ones. Why had Fearless given up an economics course, in 1964, to join the guerrillas? Why had the Commissar given up Caxito, his old father a poor peasant ruined by the theft of the coffee country, and come? Perhaps the Commissar did have a clearer reason than the rest of them. Why had the Operations Chief given up Dembos? Why had Miracle given up his family? Why had Muatianvua, uprooted, a sailor, given up the ships to march on foot now, in a life of adventure so different from the one he knew? And why had he, Theory, given up his wife and the position he could so easily acquire? Political consciousness, awareness of the needs of the people! Easy words, words that basically said nothing. How did this so-called consciousness affect each of them?

His companions were beginning to stir to wakefulness, and the teacher had not put these thoughts aside. Mayombe did not allow the dawn to enter, although outside it had already broken. The night birds yielded the stage to the chorus of monkeys and squirrels. And the waters of the Lombe lowered their voice, in waiting for their gilded cloak. In front as the Lombe descended, less than a day's march away, must be the enemy.

I, THE NARRATOR, AM THEORY.

Manuela smiled at me and plunged into the bush, into the thick Amboim bush, where the coffee was peeping, wealth of mankind. The red coffee coloured the green of the forest. So Manuela coloured my life.

Manuela, Manuela, where are you now? In Gabela? Manuela from Gabela, running through the Amboim bush, the green bush with its deadly snakes, like Mayombe, but giving birth to the red fruit of coffee, the wealth of mankind.

5

Manuela, lost forever. She became another's true-love, because I left her, because Manuela was not strong enough to keep me back in Amboim and I chose Mayombe, its lianas, its secrets and its exiles.

I lost Manuela to win the right to be 'maybe', coffee with milk, a compound, hybrid, what you will. Labels are not important, labels are useful only for the ignorant who cannot tell by its colour what liquid is contained in the bottle.

Between Manuela and my own self, I chose the latter. What a tragedy it is always to have to choose, to follow one path rather than another, yes or no! Why has the World no room for maybe? I am in Mayombe, and I renounce Manuela, for the purpose of finding in the Manichaean Universe room for maybe.

I ran away from her, did not see her again, made my choice alone, shut up in the house, in our house, in that house where soon there would be a child living, crying and laughing. I never saw that child, will never see the child. Nor Manuela. My story is one of an alienated man who alienates himself in the hope of finding freedom.

When I was still a child, I wanted to be white, so that the whites would not call me black. As a man, I wanted to be black, so that the blacks would not hate me. Where do I stand then? And Manuela, how could she fit into the life of someone haunted by the problem of choice, of yes or no? I ran away from her, yes I ran away from her, because she was too much in my life; my life is the task of showing to all and sundry that there is always room for maybe.

Manuela, Manuela, another's true-love, giving her caresses to another man. And here am I, soaked by the incessant woman-rain, weary, exiled, in despair, without Manuela.

Fearless went to wash alongside the Commissar. He admired the other man's slim, muscular torso.

'You're in good shape. I'm beginning to put on a pot belly.'

'It's the outdoor life,' the Commissar said. 'It's nearly six months since you went into action . . . What annoys me is advancing without knowing for certain what one's going to do. I don't like the plan.'

The Commander sat on a rock.

'Let's hope that Ops is right. He is making the reconnaissance . . .'

6

'Reconnaissance!' the Commissar snapped. 'He followed the river down, found the timber felling track. You call that a reconnaissance? We don't even know if the Portuguese have troops around the felling.'

'We'll soon know. What matters is to make a start. We've put a Base in the interior, which is already a step forward. Border skirmishing is done with! Now let's get on with seeing things on the ground and making decisions bit by bit. In any event this operation ties in with your concepts: political rather than military action. I don't know what you're complaining about . . .'

'That's not it, Commander. If we prevent this exploitation from taking away our timber, that's striking an economic blow against the enemy, fine. There again, we'll be attacking at a new point, which is good in regard to the people, who hardly think about us . . . at least that's how it seems. But I'm worried about the military aspect. We don't know where the enemy is and in what strength. We are so few that we cannot afford the luxury of being caught on the hop. No other victory would excuse this defeat.'

The Commander soaped his face and ducked down to the fresh river water. Then he gazed at the first fishes that appeared.

'As always, you are right. But it's this unknown side of the operation that attracts me. I don't like things too neatly planned, because there is always some detail missing. I realize it's a mistake, but what would you have? It's my anarchist streak, you would say. How will we come to know the enemy? Only by making him leave the barracks, as we don't have any information. This inertia, this apathy, must end. We must liven things up. We've already been stuck too long waiting for orders. It's for us to take the decision. Action is the only way to bring to light our failings and weaknesses of organization. Why is the war progressing in other Regions and always falling back here? Because we have not been up to the mark, we, the Movement. The blame is put on the people, for treachery. An easy excuse! Are the people here treacherous or are we incompetent? Or both? To find out, we have to act, to stir things up, to break the obsolete mould which blocks development of the struggle.'

The Commissar put on his shirt. He now sat on a rock and stared at Fearless. Other guerrillas were washing further off.

'I agree we must act. I don't believe in this legend of the people's

7

treachery, it was our fault. But I think we must study the matter more carefully, not act in haste. Above all now that we are making war without the people, in isolation . . .'

'Castaways on an island called Mayombe,' Fearless said.

'Above all now that we are weak, that we are absurdly under strength, we must be cautious. Our plans must be perfect. Action certainly, it is the only thing to sharpen the contradictions that take us forward, but conscious action. We are blind, since we do not have eyes and antenna, that the people provide. If we are blind, we must feel out the way before moving ahead, or we may fall down a hole.'

They had finished washing. Fearless lit a cigarette. The smell of the breakfast gruel reached them. The Commissar coughed and said:

'You are the Commander, your will is law . . .'

'There are three of us in Command, comrade. If you two were not in agreement, I would budge. I'm not a dictator, as you well know.'

'Three of us? There are two of you!'

Fearless stared. A wrinkle showed between his eyes.

'What do you mean?'

'Simply that as soon as you and I disagree, there are two of you and one of me. Ops is always on your side. One might think you had never noticed!'

'Sure, I've noticed. Why does he do that?'

'Haven't you any idea?'

'I have two ideas: either because I am Commander, or because you are Commissar.'

'You are teasing!'

'Not in the least. Either because I am Commander and he must support me to keep my goodwill for his promotion . . . or because you are Commissar, in the post above his, and he must oppose you, destroy you, show up your mistakes, to take your place.'

'Is that what you think?'

'Certainly!'

'I think so too,' the Commissar said. 'It's a pity! He's a good soldier, in my opinion. Especially when I'm not taking part in an operation and so his initiatives cannot add to my prestige. When I am there, he makes mistakes just to contradict me. It's not that I am always right, but I am sometimes . . .'

8

The Commander clapped him on the back.

'You must adjust to men and not to ideals. That's why the Commissar's role is so thorny. The odd thing is that you, in your tribe, even forget you belong to the same tribe, when there's competition for a job.'

'Unfortunately that does not mean that we don't have tribalism. And you are not going to try to tell me that it isn't the same with Kikongo?'

'Am I Kikongo? Are you Kimbundu? Do you still think so?'

'Not us. We belong to the minority who have already forgotten our roots and the village we came from. Or who mix it up with other villages we have known. But what about the majority, Commander, the majority?'

'That's your job: to show the comrades so many villages that they will be lost if, one day, they return to their own. This art of disorientation is called political training!'

And they went off to take their gruel.

I, THE NARRATOR, AM THEORY.

My learning led me to be appointed teacher at Base. At the same time I am a political instructor, assisting the Commissar. My life at Base is taken up with classes and with guards. Sometimes, and rarely, action. As soon as we go to the interior, there is more activity. Not activity of war, but patrol and reconnaissance. I always volunteer for missions, even against the Command's wish: could I refuse? At once they would remember that I am not the same as the others.

Once I wanted to avoid going on reconnaissance: I had a foreboding of doom. There were so few at Base that my silence would have been noted straightaway. I volunteered. That is total alienation. The others can equivocate, can argue when they are picked. How could I do that, when I bear in me the original sin of a white father?

Struggle did not agree with the proposal of his group chief, Truth. As soon as the Commander appeared, Struggle said:

9

'Comrade Commander, comrade Truth thinks that we should capture the timber workers and shoot them, because they work for the colonialists. He says that's what was decided.'

The Commander sat down and put his spoon on the pan lid, without replying. The Commissar leaned against a tree, and went on eating as he watched the group.

'Leave off, mate!' Muatianvua said. 'These workers are Cabindas, and that's why you're angry. But they're still traitors, even if they were Lundas or Kimbundus . . .'

'How come?' said Struggle, flustered. 'The Diamang workers? Those at Cotonang? Are they traitors? They have to work for the colonialist . . .'

'Right, they are, mate,' Muatianvua said. 'After the war has gone on so long, those who are not for us are against us. This lot here are right by the Congo. They may even be listening to our broadcasts. They see there's exploitation. So why don't they join us? Leave it! Just a clean sweep, mate!'

Miracle waited for Struggle's reaction. As the latter was hurt and did not reply, Miracle addressed the Commissar:

'What does comrade Commissar think?'

'I think we should go, there's nothing to be said. We'll talk about it later. But there'll be trouble for any man who touches a worker or civilian without orders. Trouble for him!'

'Muatianvua is joking with Struggle,' the Commander said. 'These ruffians are always fooling over serious things . . .'

Muatianvua laughed and lit a cigarette. He winked at Struggle.

'But the Commissar's warning is serious,' Fearless went on. 'Anyone who tries to use tribalism against the Cabinda people will be shot. Shot. We are not joking.'

The heavy silence that followed Fearless's declaration was not brushed aside, like the creepers that hit us in the face. The silence was Mayombe, perpetually present, in the innumerable creepers that are brushed aside.

They went straight on, criss-crossing the river to shorten the route. The first minutes were a torment for Theory. Now the going was easier. He had won the first battle, the toughest. He knew that he would now win the whole battle. They advanced at a distance from each other, in Indian file, between the broad manioc leaves where elephants lurked. The odour of elephant was constant. A pity we did not come to hunt, thought Ekuikui, the hunter; it would provide food for a long while. And as they crossed the river again, they came across a herd of elephants. Instinctively, Ekuikui raised his weapon.

'Don't anyone shoot!' the Operations Chief yelled.

Ekuikui gazed at the elephants who moved off calmly, waving their trunks and huge ears, and unperturbed by the file of men in green emerging from the immense green of Mayombe. The Commissar clapped him on the back:

'We've come in search of tuga*. If we fire, the tuga might hear and be alerted.'

Ekuikui, the hunter from Bie, nodded sadly.

'I know, comrade Commissar.'

Struggle was pondering the argument with his comrades. The Commander had said it had been a joke. From Muatianvua, yes; but Truth was not joking. Struggle went on absent-mindedly, at the head of the column, leading it through virtually unknown territory. Soon they would reach the track used for carrying the felled trees. These people too who did not give support! Just for shooting. His father, mother, brothers? All to be shot? The people did not give support, because the war had not grown. The people did not give support, because they had come to wage war in Cabinda without explaining beforehand what they were doing, when Struggle was still a child.

As they rounded a hill, they caught the buzz of a mechanical saw, through the myriad buzzes of Mayombe. The sound came from the right, very close by. But Struggle, self-absorbed, kept moving forward.

'What's the matter with him?' the Commander whispered to Ekuikui.

Struggle was moving away from the rest of the group, who had frozen on hearing the sound. The Commissar ran after him, avoiding making much noise.

'He's doing it on purpose,' said Miracle.

'He's going to warn the men,' said Pangu-Akitina.

---

* Tuga, a slang abbreviation of the word for Portuguese, was used pejoratively to indicate the colonial settlers and soldiers; and in the guerrilla name Ungrateful Tuga, is an irony.

Translator's note.

11

'He's going to sabotage the mission,' said Truth.

'Shut up, blast you!' the Commander said. 'Think before you speak.'

The Operations Chief had followed the Commissar. Struggle stopped when he heard his name called from behind. He was astonished to see the Commissar's angry expression, and further back the Operations Chief. At a gesture from the Commissar, he took in the loud buzz.

'Why did you go forward?'

'I wasn't thinking. Where are the rest?'

'Let's go back. And pay attention.'

The Operations Chief said nothing; he let them pass and contented himself with following. The guerrillas eyed Struggle with suspicion, but he did not notice.

'What was it?' Fearless asked.

'He was absent-minded and did not notice anything,' the Commissar said.

The Commander gave a brief smile.

'We have an idea of the scope of the Region. Okay. Truth and Mautianvua go to the left, with the Commissar. Miracle, Pangu-Akitina and Ops go to the right. We'll stay here. See what there is and come back. Take care, no shooting! We need to know if there are any soldiers.'

Fearless sat, and was soon imitated by some of his companions. Theory rubbed his knee. Ekuikui studied the trees, in search of signs of monkeys. He did it by habit, as his past as a hunter in the Central Highlands had taught him. New World, seated, was cleaning his nails with a sheath-knife. His hands were slender with long nails. A perfect intellectual, thought Fearless. Struggle moved away from the group, his ears pricked. The buzz from the saw went on cutting the air. Suddenly, the saw stopped and shouts were audible.

The guerrillas took up position. Sounds of breaking branches and, then, a crash that blanketed all the tumult of Mayombe and echoed through the tree canopy, until it was gradually lost in the Lombe valleys.

'It was a tree falling,' the Commander said.

He went and sat down again. The others remained standing, except for Theory. After a while the buzz of the saw reached them anew.

'Back to normal,' said New World. And he too sat down.

Struggle was nervous and worried, Fearless noted. Theory is in pain, but pretending not to be. Ekuikui ... he never changes. Ungrateful is suspicious of Struggle. New World must be thinking about Europe and his Marxist-Leninists. The Commander's thoughts went no further. They were snaps he took of members of the group and sorted into a mental file, without thinking any more of it. When need arose, he used the information to build a reliable picture of each guerrilla and to know what task to entrust to each of them.

The first group to arrive was the Operations Chief's. He came up to the Commander and said:

'We saw six workmen. No soldiers.'

'Were they the ones who felled the tree?'

'No. This lot have axes. The saw is with the group on the left. Behind them is a track for the transport of timber.'

'Fine.'

'Commander, I think it best to keep an eye on Struggle.'

'Why?'

'I don't believe in that absent-mindedness. He was more likely going to warn the workers, to drive them off . . .'

The Commander eyed him in silence. He pursed his lips. The other went on:

'There are times when he behaves oddly. His eyes are shifty. The Commissar doesn't notice these things, and was quick to take his word. I think he should be questioned.'

The Commander gave no reply. He was thinking of his mad desire to smoke. There he could not, the smell of a cigarette would seep through the forest.

When the Commissar's group arrived, Fearless got to his feet.

'Well then?'

'Eight workers, then a white driving the lorry. No soldiers in sight.'

'And the lorry?'

'Parked there, with the whitey smoking and listening to the radio. Further over there must be a bulldozer to load the timber trunks onto the lorry. What shall we do?'

13

The Commander called the Operations Chief. The three met.

'What do you think should be done?' Fearless asked Ops.

'I think we should make a detour, to pick up the track further ahead and reach the road.'

'And you, Commissar?'

The Commissar weighed his words, before speaking.

'I think we should seize this opportunity. We could take the workers, recover the saw, which is light to carry, and destroy the bulldozer and lorry. It would be an effective action and that was our aim. Why change?'

The Operations Chief interrupted:

'We are soldiers. We must fight the enemy. So I think the first action in this area must be military. Their soldiers must be moving at will on the road. Surely this track leads to the road. An ambush would be much better. As for the workmen? I don't see how they matter. If it were still a matter of shooting them ... But no. To politicize them! Do you think we're going to politicize anything? Here it is only war that politicizes.'

The Commander said:

'Commissar, I know that a political and economic operation is useful. The difficulty is as follows: if we destroy this equipment, military action is stymied, as the tuga will be warned that we are moving about here ...'

'Obviously,' the Commissar cut in. 'But that will be a further reason for them to be moving on the road. They must increase their patrols because there are people living here and they want to cut us off from them. They will be moving about still more and this will give us more opportunity to take a smack at them. Where's the difficulty? We won't kill twenty in the first ambush, because they will be more alert? All right, we'll kill ten. A people's war is not measured by the number of enemy dead. It is measured by the degree of popular support it has.'

'That support is won with weapons alone,' Ops said.

'Not alone. With two things. With weapons md by politicization. We must first show that we are not bandits, that we do not kill the people. The people here don't know us, have heard only enemy propaganda, are afraid of us. If we take the workers, treat them well,

14

discuss with them, and then later, have a good go at the tuga, that way, certainly, the people will begin to believe and to accept us. But it is slow work. Anyway, this action doesn't stop us mounting an ambush as well.'

'It's a question of time and food supply,' Fearless said.

'Our comrades will put up with a little hunger, if we explain the advantage.'

'Fine,' the Commander said. 'Let's do as you wish. We'll surround the groups, take them prisoner, destroy what we can, capture the saw, etc. Then we retreat with the workers and study the possibility of returning to the road to mount an ambush. I'll go with two men to a position on the track, near the lorry. If it takes off, we'll finish it. If troops appear from the road, we'll stop them. Each of you will go in the direction you reconnoitred. Keep the noise down. Encircle them and, at ten on the dot, capture them. Synchronize watches. The rendezvous is here, if there is nothing new. If the tuga show up, we will rendezvous where we slept last night.'

'Who does Struggle go with?' Ops asked.

'With me,' said Fearless.

The Operations Chief's team set off straightaway. The other two teams went together towards the workmen. The Commander, Struggle and Theory then went along the track, to close the circle. The saw buzzed and covered the sounds of trodden leaves. Even the birds were deceived and did not fly away.

The Commissar, followed by his men, advanced cautiously. Dry leaves crackled under their boots, but the crackle was drowned by the noise of the saw eating into Mayombe. The guerrillas ensconced themselves by a huge fallen tree-trunk. The felled monster had given up breathing, and its cut branches bestrewed the soil. After the saw had cut off its life support, the axes had come and lopped off legs, arms, coat; there it was, with pale white skin, a giant which once stayed the wind and hurled challenges at the clouds. Motionless but dignified. In its agony it had torn up shoots, bushes, and lianas, and its death roar had made Mayombe quaver, and silenced apes and leopards.

The guerrillas spread out for the advance. The mechanical saw – a bee boring into an ant-hill – went on with its task. There was a

15

mechanic operating the saw, and an assistant with a can of petrol and one of oil; further back were four workmen with axes. All were so absorbed in their task that they did not notice the stealthy shadows. Nor could they utter a shout when they saw the Pepesha muzzles trained on them. Their eyes opened wide, the saucer-white of their eyes swallowed up their face, with mouth gaping in a shout that dared not emerge but remained inwardly vibrating. The Commissar and Ekuikui advanced to the saw. Ekuikui poked the muzzle of his weapon into the mechanic's back:

'Don't move!'

The mechanic looked over his shoulder and swiftly took in the situation. He stopped the saw. The silence that followed pierced the guerrillas' ears, soared over the canopy of the trees and hovered, mingling with the mist that covered Mayombe.

'All of you over here, move!' the Commissar ordered.

They gathered the prisoners, searched them for weapons; removed two pocket knives.

'Are there any more men?' the Commissar asked.

'There,' the mechanic muttered, pointing at the spot to which the Operations Chief had gone.

'Soldiers?'

'Only at the barracks. Ten kilometres away.'

'The white man?'

'He's in the lorry.'

'Let's go. And don't try to escape, no harm will come to you.'

The cortege left in the direction of the rendezvous. Muatianvua kept an eye on the mechanic, who was carrying the saw. The other workmen were shaking.

When the saw stopped buzzing, the Operations Chief's team had not yet encircled the workers who in pairs were using their axes on the colossuses of Mayombe. Pangu-Akitina, who was leading, stopped immediately: they were ten metres from the first pair of workers; the other pairs were at a distance from each other. The silence attracted the attention of the workmen, who made signs to each other, in expectation of the fall of a tree. The guerrillas waited, with hearts in their mouths, for work to resume. But no crash of a falling tree came and the oldest workman said:

16

'Something's up. The motor stopped for no reason.'

They all pricked up their ears. The guerrillas stopped breathing, shrinking into the green of the undergrowth. One of the workmen further off put down his axe and came up to the pair nearest the guerrillas. The Operations Chief assessed the situation: he must act quickly.

'Don't move an inch!' he shouted, as he jumped towards the old workman.

Surprise froze those who were nearest. But the rest threw down their axes and ran towards the bush. Some of the guerrillas chased after them.

'Don't fire!' New World shouted, as he ran after the fugitives.

But the Operations Chief, to frighten the workmen, fired a burst up into the leaves.

Miracle, leaping over the fallen trunks, was hard on a workman's heels. Suddenly, there was a slope and a stream. The workman plunged in and went crawling over the stones in the shallow river. Miracle raised his bazooka and hesitated: should he waste a shell in the air to stop him? The workman, scraping his belly along the stones, disappeared round a bend in the stream, and Miracle turned back, taking as a trophy a machete that had fallen from the man's belt.

New World fired into the air and the workman he was chasing halted, on trembling legs. It was a mere boy. Affectionately, almost tenderly, New World led him to the group of three other prisoners.

'Where is the bulldozer?' Ops asked.

The eldest worker pointed out the direction. He had one leg crippled. A tree must have fallen on him, thought New World.

'Take us there.'

The group moved forward to the spot on the track where Fearless must be.

The silence when the saw suddenly stopped did not disturb the thoughts of the Portuguese, who was seated at the lorry wheel. He had even lit a cigarette, as Fearless could make out. But, when the first burst roared out, the tuga woke from his doze and was alert in every nerve. Without waiting to find out what was happening, he started the lorry and drove off. Twenty metres away, in ambush, the

17

guerrillas observed him. Fearless saw that the white was sweating and making grimaces, as he accelerated.

'Hold fire!' Fearless shouted.

Struggle was about to protest.

'Aim for the wheels only!'

It was at this moment that the second burst, fired by New World, could be heard, and it merged with Struggle's burst. One tyre went, but the lorry was already away and continued over the junction. The tuga ground the accelerator, and his clenched hands gripped the wheel.

Struggle turned to Fearless.

'Why? . . .'

'He was a civilian.'

'And the bulldozer?' Theory reminded them.

The three ran to the place where the bulldozer should be. Then they came across the Operations Chief's team.

'Did you let whitey get away?' the latter asked.

'Yes. And we gave him a pass as well,' Fearless said, angrily.

The bulldozer driver had gone into the bush, on hearing the first burst. The guerrillas surrounded the bulldozer.

'Put a bazooka into it and then set it on fire,' the Commander ordered. A workman timidly asked permission from New World to be excused. And he was holding his stomach.

'Crap here!' said New World.

The explosion from the bazooka was like the fall of a giant. When the smoke cleared, the bulldozer motor was seen to be destroyed completely. The stink of powder was mixed with a more typical stink. New World looked at Fearless and the latter looked at the workman who had asked to be excused.

'This chump . . .' was all Fearless had time to exclaim.

Suddenly, he doubled up in a wave of laughter that roared through Mayombe. Fearless's laughter was an immeasurable rebuke to the plant god who made their voices sound like whispers. The guerrillas thought at first that the firing of a bazooka so close had turned Fearless's head. Then they saw the workman standing, with his legs apart, in a fixed stare of relief, with faeces sliding down his legs and dripping to the ground.

The Commander, regaining self-possession, gave a look of distaste and ordered that the bulldozer be set on fire, as nothing could be salvaged. They gathered firewood, stacked it round the machine, soaked the wood in petrol and put a match to it. The flames swiftly licked upwards to the nearest branches of the trees. Two guerrillas led the four workmen to a more remote spot, from where they could see nothing, while Ungrateful Tuga placed three anti-personnel mines close to the bulldozer. When the mines were well camouflaged, Fearless wrote on a scrap of paper:

> BASTARD COLONIALISTS,
> GO TO HELL, GO HOME.
> WHILE YOU ARE HERE,
> IN SOMEONE ELSE'S LAND,
> THE BOSS IS ENJOYING YOUR WIFE
> OR SISTER, THERE IN THE GREENS!

And he left the message well in sight, in the middle of the mine-field. The guerrillas smiled.

'Any bastard who wants to read that will go up in the air,' Ops said.

'It was a shame not to boost the mines with dynamite,' Ungrateful said, 'but there wasn't time.'

'Let's go,' Fearless said.

The group went on through Mayombe, with the prisoners in the middle, on their way to the rendezvous.

At the rendezvous, they counted the prisoners taken by the two teams: ten. Fearless noticed that the mechanic looked more knowledgeable than the rest. He asked him:

'Where does the track lead?'

'To the road.'

'What road?'

'Between Sanga and Nguembo's Fall. The road is five kilometres away.'

'How many soldiers are there at the barracks?'

The mechanic hesitated. He looked at his companions. They had no idea.

'Don't know. Perhaps a hundred . . .'

'Tuga?'

'And Angolans. Special Forces . . .'

The questioning went on and was extended to the other prisoners. The lad New World had captured was fourteen and named Antonio. He was speaking more willingly than the rest. The mechanic was doubtful, and his eyes moved nervously from one to the other, but mainly to Fearless. Struggle asked for permission to speak to them in Fiote, but Ops replied it was not worth the bother. The Commissar was going to step in. Fearless gripped him by the arm, and pressed for silence. Fearless went on with the questioning in Portuguese, a language all understood, more or less.

Then the Command had a meeting. It was decided to hold the workers for a day, as they took the route to the Congo. Then they would set the workers free and come back to the same position, between the track and the road. The tuga would not dare come near that day. On the next day, the workers would go and say that the guerrillas had returned to the Congo and the soldiers would fall into an unexpected ambush. This would make them believe that several groups were operating there.

'They are used to our launching an action then retreating to the Congo, and will never realize that it's the same group,' Fearless said. 'This will have an impact on the morale of the people, to whom we'll be showing unfamiliar strength, and on the tuga, who will certainly be confused. What is essential is not to make any mistakes.'

'It's a pity that tuga escaped,' Ops said.

'What could we do? Shoot and kill him, as UPA do? He's a civilian. He looked so scared! We would not be showing courage by killing civilians, even colonialists . . . We tried to take him alive, but he ran away. All to the good! What could we do with him? Set him free like the others? There would have been a revolt among the guerrillas. Take him to the Congo? On what pretext?'

'I think you did right,' the Commissar said. 'We must not act against the civilian population, even if it is hostile. Why give the Government ammunition?'

The Operations Chief said nothing. He got up and went off to the forest.

20

'You mentioned the message you left by the bulldozer, but didn't say what it contained, Commander.'

Fearless explained what the sign said. The Commissar laughed, then said:

'Not very political!'

'What do you expect? Copying out a chunk of Marx? This is the only politics these tuga understand.'

They lunched there and then, guerrillas and workmen. The pans were passed from hand to hand. One workman had a packet of cigarettes, which he shared out to the guerrillas. As they stretched out by the Lombe, they loosened their tongues, and only then did the workmen discover that Struggle too was from Cabinda.

Now, thought Fearless, they see one of their own among us, and they feel more confident. Sometimes tribalism can help. But what is the matter with Ops that makes him so attentive to the talk? Ah! He is trying to pick up what Struggle is saying, to see if he is being treacherous. What pleasure this fellow would take in eating Struggle, fried in palm-oil . . .

I, THE NARRATOR, AM MIRACLE.

I was born in Quibaxe, a Kimbundu area, like the Commissar and the Operations Chief, who are from around there.

As bazooka-man, I love to see the trucks laden with troops halted by my marksmanship. I think there could be no greater pleasure in life.

My land is rich in coffee, but my father was always a poor peasant. I did first year school only, and learned the rest here, in the Revolution. I was a child at the time of 1961. But I still remember the spectacle of children bashed against trees, men buried to the neck, with their heads above ground, and a tractor passing to lop off their heads with a blade made to dig up the earth, to provide wealth for mankind. What pleasure I had just now in destroying that bulldozer! It was like the one that took off my father's head. The bulldozer is not to blame, depends who is driving it, it's like taking up a weapon. But I cannot lose my hatred for tractors, forgive me.

Now Struggle is talking to the workmen. Perhaps he is explaining that

21

he wanted to forewarn them, but was caught out. They're letting him talk! The Commander doesn't care, he was not in Angola in 1961, or, if he was, did not suffer. He was in Luanda, must have been a student, what does he know? And the Commissar? In such matters the Commissar is a softy, he thinks that fine words can win over the people of Cabinda, treacherous people. Only the Operations Chief . . . but he is third in command, carries no weight.

And I ran away from Angola with my mother. Still a kid. I went to Kinshasa. Then I joined MPLA, at the suggestion of my uncle, who was a leader. At the time! He isn't any more, was expelled. The MPLA expels the better ones, just because they will not let themselves be bossed by the Kikongos who move in. Poor MPLA! Only in the First Region is it still the same, the vanguard movement. And we, from the First Region, obliged to wage war here, in a stranger's area, where they don't speak our language, where the people are counter-revolutionary, so what are we doing here? Poor MPLA, a long way from our Region, can't do any good!

They marched all afternoon, climbing the Lombe. They stopped at five, to look for firewood and to pitch camp: at six, in Mayombe, it was pitch black and one could not go further.

The meal was taken in common: rice and beans, then fish that Struggle and one of the workmen had caught in the Lombe. The workmen did not try to escape, although they had lots of chances during the march. Above all when Miracle had fallen with the bazooka and the guerrillas had gone to see what had happened; some of the workmen had been left on their own and they sat down, to wait for the fighters, did not escape. Confidence brought more lively discussions.

Drawing on the clues he had garnered, the Commissar spoke to the workmen, as forks were lifting rice and beans to their destination.

'You earn twenty escudos a day, for chopping down trees with an axe, walking, walking, carrying heavy loads. The driver earns fifty escudos a day, for working with the saw. But how many trees a day does your team chop? Thirty perhaps. And how much does the boss earn for each tree? A pile. What does the boss do to earn this money? Nothing, nothing. But he's the one to profit. And the axe you use is not even his. It's yours, and you bought it at the store for seventy escudos. Is the machete his? No, you bought it for fifty escudos. This means, that not even the tools you use belong to the boss. You are obliged to purchase them, have a deduction in your salary at the end of the month. Do the trees belong to the boss? No. They are yours, they are ours, because they are in Angolan territory. Do the axes and machetes belong to the boss? No. They are yours. Does the sweat belong to the boss? No, it is yours, because you are doing the work. So, how can he earn many thousands a day and give you twenty escudos? What right has he? This is colonialist exploitation. The man who works is providing wealth for the foreigner, who does not work. The boss has might on his side, has the army, the police, the administration. He uses this might to force you to work, to enrich him. Did we do right or wrong to destroy the bulldozer?'

'You did right,' the workmen replied.

'As for this mechanical saw, to whom does it really belong? The boss bought it from the Germans, but where did he find the money to buy it? Whom did he exploit to buy the saw? Tell me.'

'The workers,' young Antonio replied.

'This saw belongs to you, belongs to the people. So it cannot be returned to the colonialist. One would give it to you, because it is yours, but what are you going to do with it? Can you sell it? Can you use it?'

'No. Better for you to take the saw,' came the reply from the oldest worker, the one with a crippled leg. 'We can't make use of it.'

'Everything that is yours, axes, machetes, knives, watches, cash, all your things, you can take them with you. And you will take the axes and machetes of the men who ran away, to deliver them back. But what belongs to the colonialist will stay with us. The tuga say that we are bandits, that we kill the people, that we steal. Have we done you any harm? Did we kill anyone? Even the white man, we could have killed him, but we did not want to. We are not bandits. We are soldiers who are struggling so that the trees you chop down may serve the people and not the foreigner. We are struggling so that the petrol in Cabinda may serve to enrich the people and not the Americans. But as we struggle against the colonialists, and they know that, after our victory, they will forfeit the wealth they steal from the people,

23

they tell you we are bandits, so that the people will be afraid of us and denounce us to the army.'

The discussion rambled on, sometimes in Portuguese with the Commissar and Theory, sometimes in Fiote with Struggle. The workmen reported what they knew about barracks in the Region, living conditions, what the inhabitants felt. Fearless listened, but he was attentive also to the comments from the rest of the guerrillas. The latter divided by and large into two groups: Kimbundus around the Operations Chief, and the others in a group, those who were not Kimbundu: Kikongos, Umbundus and the detribalised such as Muatianvua, born in Lunda of an Umbundu father and Kimbundu mother. New World was from Luanda, from a Kimbundu background, but studying or perhaps the stay in Europe had freed him from tribalism. He kept aloof, cleaning his weapon by the firelight.

When they had settled down, the Commissar asked in a half-whisper:

'So, what do you think of the operation?'

'You talk better than a preacher,' Fearless said. 'If they didn't believe you, at least they are too polite to show it ... I agree, we should do more actions of this kind, these people could be mobilized. If we had a solid organization here, yes. But what do you want? With the level of organization we have, with the nonsense that goes on, these actions are too reminiscent of Seminary vows. That's why I spoke of you as a preacher. It is as if you were promising eternal life in the Hereafter, when on Earth you were doing the utmost to make life unbearable.'

'I don't follow you.'

'When I was at the Seminary, one thing always puzzled me, rang a false note. It was this false note that drove me to sacrilege, and, later, to atheism. Why did the fathers, so chaste, so kind-hearted and so holy, who were preparing us to serve God, to be worthy of God, by promising us the delights of celestial life, lead us such a miserable life in the Seminary, and why were they so arbitrary, so cruel, so sadistic in the tortures they invented for our benefit? This led me into desiring what horrified them, to want to know what they feared, to seek out what they forbade us to see or hear or feel. It was with a mixture of holy terror, carnal delight and joyous vengeance that I had my first

24

woman. Right in the Seminary, in an annexe; she was a servant who provided relief for seminarists and, who knows, some of the fathers. I was fourteen. I went to confession the following morning and concealed the deed, as I would have been expelled: already I had lost belief in the seal of the confessional. And I took communion in a state of mortal sin, because if I had not, it would have been spotted that something was going on. And I went on confessing, without the courage to expunge the sacrilege. And I went on meeting the servant-girl in annexes and took increasing pleasure in love-making, above all because the love-making was perverse, tainted by a sacrilege I would never redeem. Eventually when I was sixteen, and out of the Seminary – I was finally expelled for striking a white priest who practised overt racism – the fear of Hell became unbearable; I felt damned, persecuted for a thousand crimes and all the unworthy pleasures in which I had indulged. The certainty that I was lost was so great that I decided Hell did not exist, could not exist, or I would be damned. Either I should deny it, destroy what persecuted me, or I would go mad with fear. I slew God, slew Hell and slew the fear of Hell. That's where I learned that enemies must be confronted, it is the only way to find inner peace.'

'I don't see the connection,' the Commissar said.

'Nor I. I saw it at the beginning, now I don't know why I said all that. But when you were talking, promising freedom, you made me remember the Seminary, and what have you.'

And he covered his head with the blanket, and fell at once into deep sleep.

The Commissar stayed pondering Fearless's words, gazing at the flames from the fire that changed the appearance of men and things, and inspired confidences.

◆

After breakfast, they took their leave of the workmen, returning all their belongings to them. Not all, since it proved impossible to find a hundred-escudo note they had taken from the mechanic's pockets, and which was in the keeping of Ekuikui. They searched Ekuikui's pockets, clothing, pack, and did not find it. Ekuikui was wailing, saying that at night it had still been in his pocket, and he had wanted to hand it to the Commissar, but the latter said it was not worth the bother, should remain with Ekuikui and be returned in the morning to the owner. During the night it had disappeared, someone had stolen it, the ex-hunter complained. But he had not hidden it, would never steal from one of the people, knew what this meant for the Movement. They took their leave of the workmen, with the mechanic saying that it was not important, a small sum of money. What he wanted was to see himself free and the matter of the note was delaying departure and freedom.

When the guerrillas had advanced about a kilometre up river, the Commander called a halt.

'Meeting. Let's sit down.'

The guerrillas complied. Fearless went on:

'We are going back again to mount an ambush on the road. The workmen will say that we returned to the Congo and the tuga will not expect to find us on the road. But we must make good time. Obviously we do not have enough food for these extra days we are spending away from Base. We must make sacrifices. But, if the operation really comes off, the Command think it is worth the trouble of spending a couple of days without eating. If you comrades agree. Do you agree to put up with a little bit more and have a really hefty go at the tuga?'

Without exception, the guerrillas agreed whole-heartedly. It was a long time since they had clashed with the colonial army.

'Good,' Fearless said, with a smile. 'Then we must let the workmen get a good distance ahead. Meanwhile, let us use the chance to look at this matter of the hundred escudos. This is serious, because it could give the lie to all we say. It means, in effect, that we are bandits, that we steal from the people. The bastard who hung onto the money is a counter-revolutionary, besides being a cheap crook, since he sabotaged all the good impression we could have made on the workers. It would be better if he would say now where the money is . . . Later on it will be worse!'

No-one spoke. The Commissar reinforced the Commander's words. No-one made a sign. The Commander ordered them to come to him

26

one by one, to be searched. It was then that the Operations Chief spoke:

'As I understand, it was Ekuikui who had the money. Why do you think it was not him but somebody else? He could have buried the note, or hidden it in a tree, so as not to be found in a search. What's more, it should all have been with the Commissar, he should have looked after it. Now, to search everybody ... Shows suspicion, it's an insult!'

'I know it's my fault,' the Commissar burst out. 'Obviously it's my fault for not keeping the money, as I kept the watches. Yes, it's my fault. But now what we must do is search everybody. We've already searched Ekuikui, let's do it to everyone. It's no insult, but we all pay for one.'

Meanwhile, Fearless was not looking at the Commissar's excited expression or the Operations Chief's cold eyes. Fearless was studying the reaction of each of the guerrillas.

'I don't agree with the suspicion against the guerrillas,' Ops said, eliciting from the mouths of some fighters murmurs of approval. 'If someone in charge makes a mistake, why should the mistake give rise to suspicion against the guerrillas? Why are all the guerrillas shamed, all, just for the sake of one? If the mistake is by someone in charge?'

'That's enough!' shouted Fearless. 'A mistake by someone in charge does not justify theft, theft of a lousy hundred, by a wretched saboteur. Let's make the search. Wars are not won with demagogy, merely to win support from the bases! Struggle, come here.'

But Fearless was not looking at Struggle, who came forward with his pack open. Fearless stared at the group behind.

The Commissar searched Struggle and the pack, and anywhere a hundred-escudo note could be put. Struggle was dressing, when Fearless, bellowing, gave a mighty leap to the ground behind. He gripped an arm of Ungrateful Tuga, who tried to wrench free, and a hundred-escudo note fell to the ground.

'Bastard!' gasped Fearless. 'I suspected you from the start.'

He dragged Ungrateful into the middle of the group and said:

'He was the one sleeping next to Ekuikui. Now, he was trying to bury the note, to collect it later. But I was watching. Tell us, how did you get hold of this note?'

It was useless to dissemble, dangerous even. Ungrateful Tuga admitted that he had slept next to Ekuikui and had seen in which pocket the ex-hunter had kept the note. He had stolen it during the night. The guerrillas did not say anything, some were on Ungrateful's side, some opposed.

'You will be tried when we reach Base. Your weapon will remain with Ekuikui, who will guard you. Beware if he runs away! You will be tried in his place. What kind of guerrilla have you turned out to be, to let yourself be robbed? Don't you sleep with one eye open?'

'I was very tired yesterday, comrade Commander. I slept too deeply . . .'

'Commander, how are we going to find the workmen again?' Struggle said. 'They must be far away by now, it's not possible!'

'I suggest the best thing is to try to contact the people after the attack,' Theory proposed. 'We shall think out how, calmly. We have the man's name and the village's, perhaps we can manage to go there and hand it over.'

'Very risky,' Ops said.

'I will volunteer to go,' the Commissar said. 'I was to blame for what happened, I know how important the political aspect is . . .'

'We'll consider that later,' Fearless said. 'Now we shall advance. But carefully. If, by chance, the tuga follow us and try to see where we are going, we may meet face to face. So it's better to take another route, as we are not in a hurry to arrive.'

Struggle took the lead in the column, which followed with Ungrateful Tuga in the middle and disarmed, which was risky when the enemy might appear at any moment.

The men were beginning to show signs of fatigue; they had left Base four days earlier and provisions would soon run out, as they had been obliged to share them with the workers. These were facts to be borne in mind, mused Fearless, his AK held by the muzzle and draped carelessly over his shoulder, his Cuban cap hiding the bullet scar on his forehead (from the time when he was surprised by the enemy in the river, when he was bathing; he had to pretend to be dead, which was sustained by the blood that ran from his forehead and stained the river water; when the comrades reacted, he managed to hide in the rocks and make his way back to Base, naked; he was ticked off by

28

Command, by Henda, since his canteen and ammunition belt were recovered by the enemy; not the weapon, which his companions had taken). After an hour's march, Fearless ordered a stop.

'Let's fish, we must have food.'

Most of the provisions were tinned (corned beef, sardines, a little milk), the rest was rice and manioc.

Struggle always carried hooks and line. He and New World ensconced themselves by a rock, while the others spread out in groups on the Lombe, to wash or chat. Fearless enjoyed these breaks on a march, when he mused to himself, as he gazed at the trees, or when he sounded out the character of his companions. Seeing Theory on his own and rubbing his knee, the Commander went up and sat by him.

'Does it hurt?'

'Slightly. It's getting better.'

Fearless lit a cigarette, one of the last he had left. He closed his eyes, the better to savour the inhalation.

'When I was a kid, before I went to study at the Seminary, something happened to me. I must have been about eight. I got in a row with an older boy and the bloke beat me up. I ran away in fear. I abandoned the fight. For days, I felt a disgrace, a coward, a weakling, felt that any kid could beat me and I would run . . .'

He was silent a moment, observing the teacher: Theory listened, inscrutable. Fearless went on:

'I decided then that, to win back my self-respect, there was only one thing to do: seek revenge. I provoked him again, you can't imagine how scared I was, knew that I would take a beating, didn't have the slightest hope. He was much stronger and brought up on slum fights. I defended myself as best I could, more from the fear he provoked in me than from the actual blows I received. In the end it was not so painful. My nose was bleeding, that's why I have a slightly bent nose, as you can see. In the end it was not painful. He was the one who stopped, tired of fighting. I was going on to the end, ready to die if necessary, but not to surrender. He ended up saying: you've won, I give up. Since then we remained friends . . . From then on I understood that it is not the blows we suffer that hurt, it is the sense of defeat or of having been a coward. I was never able to run away

29

again. I always wanted to see to what extent I was able to overcome fear.'

'Why are you telling me this?' Theory asked.

There was something he wanted to discover in Theory, something that eluded him. He replied with another question:

'Are you always afraid?'

The other looked at him, in astonishment. Yes, in astonishment, Fearless noticed. Astonished, yet, at heart, almost relieved. In unwitting haste, as if breaking free, Theory said:

'Yes, I am always afraid. Fear haunts me. I don't know why I'm telling you, but it's the truth. I am afraid of doing guard at night, I'm afraid of battle, I'm even afraid of living at the Base . . .'

'I thought as much. And why don't you show it?'

'Show it? A man of mixed blood to show fear? Haven't you seen the effect? I've tried always to master myself, control myself . . . do you understand? It's as if I were two people: one who is frightened, always frightened, and another who always volunteers for dangerous duties, who constantly displays an iron will . . . There is one who wants to cry, to stay put, because his knee hurts, and another who says there is nothing the matter, that he can go on. Because of the others! I know that, on my own, I am a coward, would be unable to act like a man. But when the others are there, to monitor me, to spy on my reactions, to see if I make a false step and then give vent to all their racism, the second personality in me takes over and leads me into saying what I don't want, to be brave, even to excess, since I cannot retreat . . . It is hard!'

Fearless passed him the cigarette he had smoked halfway. Theory seized on it anxiously and, shaking, smoked it to the end without a pause. Fearless said softly:

'There are things a person hides, hides, and has difficulty in telling. But as soon as it is told, then everything seems clearer to us and we feel free. It is good to talk. This is the kind of thing that can destroy an individual, if he keeps it to himself. But you can be certain that all of us feel fear, the difficulty is that intellectuals exaggerate it, give it too much importance. The real root is in social class . . . We all think we have two personalities, one a coward and another, that we do not call courageous, but unconscious. Fear . . . fear is not the problem.

30

The question is to be able to control fear and overcome it. You say that you overcome it when others are watching you, or when you think they are watching you, which is more accurate . . . but, if you were alone, you would not be capable. Perhaps. You attach too much importance to what others think of you. Today, you no longer have a colour, at least in our guerrilla group you are accepted, totally accepted. Overnight you won't free yourself from this colour complex, no. But you must begin thinking that it is no longer a problem for you. You are perhaps the only one who has the sympathies and respect of all the guerrillas, I've already seen this on several occasions. You cannot live in this constant anguish, or you will have a nervous breakdown. And today there is no longer any cause.'

'My nerves have already given way so often . . .'

'Not yet. Those were just warnings! It's good to talk, it's good to chat to a friend, to whom you unburden your heart. Whenever you feel confused, come and talk to me. We'll chew it over. Bottling it up is no good, unless one is a writer. Then a fellow puts it all down on paper, in the mouths of others. But when one is not a writer, it should be released, through talk. Action is another kind of release, many of us use that method, others beat their wives or get drunk. But action as release loses all its value for me, becomes savage, irrational. The other forms are cowardice. There is only frank conversation that seems the best to me, as I am not a writer. It was not by chance that the priests invented confession, it corresponds to a human need for release. From the start religion was able to exploit certain subjective needs, and was in fact born from these needs. That is why Christianity was so readily accepted. There are some Protestant sects, I don't know if all, where confession is public. This reflects a greater level of socialization, although perhaps it leads people to be less profound, less frank, in confession. It better reflects bourgeois hypocrisy . . . Then I don't know, as I was never very frank in my personal confessions as a Catholic . . .'

Struggle had caught a big fish and the others, forgetting where they were, applauded him. The Commissar ordered them to be quiet.

'But will the fear go away?' Theory asked. 'I was never a very combatant child, never tested myself. Will I always be in a state of panic?'

31

'Your main problem is the racial complex. This affects the other, I think. If you get shot of it and understand that to hold back sometimes is not going to lower yourself in the opinion of others, who do it all the time without remorse, then you will stop feeling panic and react normally, with fear at times, without fear at others. Anyway, you've already fought often, by now you should be used to it . . .'

'And you? Do you never feel fear?'

'Me? Sometimes I do, yes. My pulse races, I feel cold, even stomach-ache. Other times, no. Usually, at moments of greatest danger, I remain calm, lucid. I always think that being scared makes it worse. That helps. But I am always looking for fear, that's true. I don't really have a fear of death, as such, in cold blood. What I do fear is dissolving into fear when I see that I am going to die, and losing my self-respect. It must be horrible to die with a feeling that the last moments of life will destroy the whole concept one has of oneself, the whole concept of oneself it has taken a lifetime to build.'

The Operations Chief came up to them, but seeing them conversing in low tones, went away. Fearless called him.

'Do you want anything?'

'Wouldn't it be better to prepare lunch?'

'Yes, yes, take this chance.'

Fearless and Theory went to help in the preparation of lunch.

After eating, they resumed the advance. They came to a mountain in front, and tackled it at two in the afternoon. The first stage of the mountain was covered in manioc leaves, which impeded the climb. Haversacks weighed down shoulders, legs were crumpling. They made frequent stops, to catch their breath. When it seemed they were near the top, a new slope appeared. The manioc leaves gave way to thick scrub, which had to be cut by machete, to open a path. At four, it began to rain. Water coursed down the mountain, soaked the ground. Boots became ten times heavier, with the weight of mud. Slips were frequent, and Pangu-Akitina, the medic, dropped his Pepesha as he slipped, and had to go and recover it twenty metres further down. By five they reached the top of the mountain, in a state of exhaustion. After a brief rest, they began the descent, since the cold made it impossible to sleep on the mountain at night. The descent, although quicker, was more dangerous than the climb. The Commissar slipped

32

and tumbled on mud, until he managed to grab hold of a creeper. Legs shook, from the effort of standing up. Knees ached. Knapsacks pushed men forward, towards the abyss. Rain continued to fall. At six it was pitch black and they had not yet descended the mountain. The remainder was almost a crawl, in the darkness of the treacherous mountain, with rain beating back into faces. If anyone should fall, the others could not be sure of finding him again. Finally they reached the river. Night did not allow them to look for a reasonably dry camp site. They let themselves fall in a kind of clearing, and checked the group to see if all were present. Fortunately, no-one was missing. They opened their packs, where everything was soaked, sleeping cloth, food, ammunition, took out tins of milk and drank the milk cold, as no fire could be lit in that heavy rain.

As he collapsed, Theory resumed rubbing his knee. The blood had now congealed. Pangu-Akitina looked at the wound, by torchlight, and left it as it was. How could he treat it, when all the dressings were soaked? He contented himself with pouring a little alcohol on the wound. Theory pursed his lips, but this did not prevent an obstinate moan escaping from his mouth.

Some stretched out a groundsheet on the wet earth to sleep. Most, however, simply stretched out on the ground and covered themselves in an already soaking sheet.

'Move your arms and legs now and then,' Fearless said to the Commissar. 'Otherwise you'll be stuck to the ground, and the climate here is so fertile that, in this rain, you'll put out roots overnight. Good-night, sweet dreams!'

'How can he still make jokes?' the Commissar asked himself, half-shocked.

I, THE NARRATOR, AM MIRACLE, THE BAZOOKA-MAN.

See how the Commander was so concerned about the hundred escudos of that Cabinda traitor? Didn't you ask why, didn't you wonder? Well I'll explain.

The Commander is Kikongo; although he went to Luanda as an infant, the truth is that his family comes from Uije. Now, Fiote and Kikongo are

33

relatives, and basically the same people. That is why he was so angry at a theft from one of his cousins. That is why he protects Struggle, another traitor. Did you see his rage when he grabbed Ungrateful? Why? Ungrateful is Kimbundu, there you have the whole story.

Intellectuals have an obsession that it is we, the peasants, who are tribalists. But they are as well. The problem is that there is tribalism and tribalism. There is legitimate tribalism, when the tribe is defended as it deserves. And there is illegitimate tribalism, when an effort is made to impose the tribe beyond the rights it deserves. It is what Lenin meant, when he spoke about just and unjust wars. One must always distinguish between just tribalism and unjust tribalism, and not speak haphazardly. It is true that all men are equal, and should all have the same rights. But all men are not at the same level; some are more advanced than others. Those who are more advanced should rule the others, they are the ones with knowledge. It is the same with tribes: the more advanced should control the others and bring them forward, until they can rule.

But what do we see here now? The most backward want to give orders. And they are going to take the key positions, while some of our lot help them. Like this idiot of a Commissar, who does not see anything that goes on. He lets himself be taken in by the Commander, is always at odds with the Operations Chief. Supposed to be intelligent, for goodness sake! He reads a lot, and, in the end, lets himself be taken in like that. Or does he do it on purpose? Sometimes I think he has an agreement with the others against us, of his own blood.

I suffered colonialism in my flesh. My father was killed by the tuga. How can I bear seeing persons who did not suffer ordering us about, as if they know what we want? This is the injustice against which we must struggle: for the authentic sons of the people, the genuine ones, to take things in hand.

It rained throughout the night. Some of the guerrillas, including Fearless, managed to sleep. The majority, however, did not close an eye, as they shivered with cold and felt rain in every part of the body.

At dawn, haggard expressions showed the weariness of successive days of effort and endurance. They drank milk only. The food was soaked, and the manioc broke up in the water. All that remained was rice and tinned stuff, and little of that.

The undergrowth was humid, the leaves still dripping. The ground was a slippery bog. They kept moving forward cross-country, until at ten they rejoined the Lombe. A patrol climbed a slope, to find directions.

They were near the road. They resumed the march, with the tiredness forgotten. As they reached the road, they heard two muffled explosions, followed shortly by another: the tuga had set off the mines by the bulldozer. The guerrillas laughed, gripping their weapons more firmly.

Moments later, the Operations Chief set out on a reconnaissance, to locate the best place to mount an ambush. It was already midday. When the Operations Chief returned, they all went forward to the chosen spot. Fearless assessed the position, gave a nod and placed his men along the road. No-one ate, just sucked a little tinned milk. The guerrillas had to be ready for anything, as soldiers might appear at any moment with those injured by the mines.

Two hours went by. Nothing. Fearless went to speak to the Commissar and Operations Chief.

'They took the wounded to the other barracks, for sure,' the Commander said. 'But there must be a patrol this way. We must hang on.'

'The last time we ate was midday yesterday,' the Commissar said. 'The comrades won't stand up much longer, after yesterday's effort ... It would be best to fall back to light a fire and cook. They will pass by tomorrow.'

'No,' the Operations Chief said, 'they will pass by today. They are bound to send reinforcements from Sanga. So, the reinforcements will go back, they won't put up with sleeping in the bush. Our comrades are standing it, spoiling for a fight. Waiting another day is worse, then we'll be right out of food.'

'You're right, Ops. Let's give it till five o clock,' the Commander said. 'If they haven't come by then, we'll pull back to camp and find firewood. There's still time!'

The Commissar was disappointed, mainly because of the glint in the Operations Chief's eyes. But he made no retort. They took up position again.

Some guerrillas were dozing, with their weapons pointed and a finger on the trigger. The Commander constantly went up and down the line of fighters, waking them gently so as not to startle them, asking trivial questions, whispering stories and anecdotes, to raise morale. The guerrillas smiled, winked at him, to show confidence. It is gratifying, Fearless was thinking, as he went from one to the other, even those who do not get on with me seem to worship me. It is the solidarity of battle!

They had returned a weapon to Ungrateful Tuga, but Ekuikui had been charged to keep a close watch on him. Ekuikui would carry out the task, with determination.

The Commander stretched out next to Theory. The teacher threw a quick glance at him, but said nothing. He knew why Fearless had come. Fearless too knew why he had come.

'Well?' the Commander asked.

'My second half is in the ascendant,' Theory said. 'Don't worry.'

'I'm not worried. I knew it.'

Fearless stood up and went along the road, to check on the guard, who was postioned two hundred metres from the ambush with instructions to give a signal when the enemy appeared.

'Shall we pull out, comrade Commander?'

'No. They will come.'

'I'm hungry, comrade Commander.'

'What about me without a cigarette all day?' Fearless replied.

He went back to the ambush point. He settled into position and waited, in a relaxed state, punctuated by checks on the time. At four, the sun could no longer be seen, as it was shaded by the trees across the road.

Waiting was the worst. Once the enemy appeared, the difficulties were over, fantasies were brushed aside, and action was all that mattered. But, in the waiting, sad memories of childhood mingled with regret for friends killed in battle and even (or mainly) the face of Leli. Fearless realized that he had gone more than six months without thinking of Leli. Since the last battle. As they went to attack the Post at Miconje, Leli's image had appeared in the rain that made torrents of mud, turning slippery the slope they were climbing to reach the enemy. They had progressed at night, under continual rainfall, to reach the point of attack at six in the morning. The mud and rain blinded them, choked them, as they gasped with the effort of crawling up a thickly wooded mountain. It was there, in the blindness of the forest and rain, that Leli came, forced her way back. The torment pursued him until he gave the order to fire. The yell to fire was like a release, the bellow of an animal running from a trap. Fearless's wounded cry had banished the image of Leli.

Once more Leli was coming, forcing her way back. Leli's eyes, at once vengeful and tender, accused him of a thousand crimes; there was such surrender and desolation in her eyes that Fearless wanted to shout out, to banish the ghost. But it was too early, the enemy had not appeared, and he could not give the order to fire. A quarter past four. Anguish gripped his belly, he felt colic pains. He forgot where he was, could not feel his body under cramped elbows, hands cradling the AK, eyes obstinately glued to the road, at the start of the bend. Leli begged and accused, mutely; words were unnecessary, he knew them, had not forgotten them. This was your revenge, to win me back in order to abandon me in the knowledge that I was once more your captive. Your pride, all of your pride, limitless pride, which sacrifices everything. He knew the words, words that had hammered through his memory a thousand times, so now Leli's eyes alone spoke.

She ran along the white beach. The palm-trees bent down to greet her. Naked, resplendent in the light of the Moon, her chestnut body was pearled with drops of water that reflected the Moon's shine. She ran along the white beach to meet him. Naked, they embraced, in the trusty shade of the palm-trees, and let themselves fall on the sand.

Sweat soaked his shirt. He felt ill, the anguish spread from his belly to his chest and he was gasping for breath. Your pride, limitless pride ... Fearless wanted to stand up and run, run as far as the enemy were, fire off all his magazines until he had wiped away the image of Leli. But the guard appeared, giving signals, and Leli vanished.

From the signals, Fearless understood that the soldiers were coming on foot, which made the operation trickier. The news spread swiftly through the guerrillas. Moments later, they heard the first voices. The tuga were cheerful at returning to barracks, noisy, carefree, convinced that the guerrillas were already in the Congo. Fearless could even make out a comment yelled by one soldier about the behaviour of another's sister. The tuga are always the same, whatever the circumstances, he thought. Will it be the one talking who falls in my volley, or the other whose sister was insulted?

The first soldiers appeared at the bend of the road. Then, gradually, the rest of the band. They came without formation, in clusters, negligently, with weapons on their shoulders. The front group entered the death zone, advanced until they were passing by the Commander. Fearless was counting the enemy soldiers. He had counted up to seventy. The guerrillas were waiting for a volley from the Commander, as a signal to open fire. The enemy vanguard was reaching the last guerrilla, while those at the tail were coming into the ambush.

Beautiful, like sitting ducks! thought Fearless. And he fired, aiming at those who were less than four metres away to his front. Immediately the Pepeshas crackled with the sound of sewing machines. Two seconds later, Miracle rose and neatly bazookaed the forward group. The soldiers, taken totally by surprise, plunged to the ground or somersaulted, after many had already fallen. Moans were lost in the rat-a-tat of Pepeshas and crump of grenades. Finally, the first soldiers began timidly to return fire, to allow those on the road to take shelter in the undergrowth.

Fearless changed magazine, just as he saw the soldier in front of him, stretched out at the roadside and feverishly trying to open the bolt of his G3. The soldier had seen him, but the weapon jammed. Fearless aimed his AK. The soldier was a frightened kid in front of him, some four metres off, with hands gripped to the bolt that would not release the spent round. Both knew what was going to happen. Inevitably, as in a tragedy, Fearless's bullet opened a neat hole in the lad's forehead and the expression of fright vanished. Inevitably, without either of them imagining any alternative.

The soldiers on the road were dead or wounded. The rest were now shooting wildly, aiming for the trees. Many were still alive, it was impossible to go on to an attack. Fearless gave order for a retreat. This was the most difficult: rounds whistled overhead, slashing the branches or burying themselves in the tree-trunks. Miracle, danger-

38

ously exposed, bazookaed a thicket from which several of the enemy were giving heavy fire. Miracle's action halted the enemy fire and the guerrillas took the opportunity to retreat, crawling out of their opponent's range. Good fighter, this Miracle, thought Fearless, as he crawled. Ten metres from the point of encounter, they could already stand and shift themselves, as there were trees in between. The colonialist soldiers raised the firing rate. The guerrillas withdrew to their rendezvous. The soldiers were hurling curses, along with the bullets, now certain that the guerrillas had gone. From Sanga the first mortar shells began to fall, fired at random, merely to demoralize.

At the rendezvous, those in charge checked the fighters: Alvorada had a slight wound in the shoulder and Muatianvua had not yet arrived. They waited for Muatianvua, while Pangu-Akitina treated the wound. Mautianvua did not show up.

'Must have been hit,' the Commissar said. 'We must go and fetch him.'

'Not possible,' Miracle said. 'I was beside him and didn't see him hit.'

'Did you see him retreat?' the Commander asked.

'No.'

'Then he could have been hit during the retreat. Who will volunteer to fetch him?'

The guerrillas looked at each other in hesitation. The soldiers were still firing and it was dangerous to go back to the ambush site, more dangerous than mounting the ambush. Struggle and Ekuikui came forward. Theory did not volunteer, Fearless noted. He is making progress, another time he would have had to volunteer, as a statement. The Commander let the two volunteers leave and then said:

'No-one wanted to volunteer, because Muatianvua is detribalised. Were he Kikongo or Kimbundu four or five would soon have come forward . . . Who did? Struggle, who is Cabinda, and Ekuikui, who is Umbundu. Detribalised, like him, since here there are no more Cabinda or Umbundu . . . Is that how we are going to win the war?'

The frightened soldier who had let his weapon jam must have been from Minho or Tras-os-Montes. And the others from Minho or Tras-os-Montes were shooting maniacally to cover him. Once they had pin-pointed from where Fearless had fired the shot which wiped away

39

the look of terror, all the men of Minho or Tras-os-Montes fired maniacally in that direction. It was to no great effect!

The two volunteers did not have to go as far as the ambush, since they met Muatianvua, calmly making his way towards the rendezvous.

'What were you hanging about for?' Fearless asked.

'Counting the dead, for the War Communiqué! There were sixteen bodies on the road, either dead or wounded, who knows? The rest were furious, cursing bitterly . . .'

'When I order retreat, that means retreat!' shouted Fearless, to convince himself. He had once done the same thing and been rebuked and commended at the same time. He soon changed his tone of voice:

'Sixteen, you say? Not bad. Let's go.'

And they went cross-country, Struggle in front, opening a path with a machete. Till six, when they came up with the Lombe again. They pitched camp there. The soldiers had ceased firing, surely out of ammunition, but the artillery at Sanga went on wasting shells. It would be like that all night. The battle had lasted two minutes, Fearless observed.

◆

They had taken the weapon from Ungrateful Tuga again. They did not post guards. At night, in the forest, the best guard was the impenetrability of Mayombe. The enemy did not know the place to which they had retreated, and so the mortar shells fell some five kilometres to the right. The mortars were, moreover, not used as weapons of attack, but merely to raise the morale of the tuga soldiers, encircled in unknown and dreadful forest that hid fearful monsters. The din calmed them, gave them a sense of power, protected them from their own fear.

The Commissar came and sat down by the Commander, and his young forehead was wrinkled. The Operations Chief was also there at his side.

'Comrade Commander, shouldn't we think about the worker's money? How are we going to return it?'

'Leave it be!' Fearless said.

'No, I can't leave it. It's important. We treated the workers well,

40

it's a long time since we had such significant contact with people in the interior, and the results could be very encouraging. But there was a shadow. A worker was robbed and knew it. The rest of them knew as well. What are the people going to say? The MPLA men treated the workers well, for sure, but only to mobilize them. As soon as they could, they stole the valuables they were carrying. What is the use of making an action like this, if we are smeared?'

'Okay. What do you suggest?'

'I should go with two comrades. We try to find the village where the mechanic lives and leave the money in a paper. Someone will find the paper and deliver it.'

'Whoever finds it will keep the money, not hand it over and finish! A risk for nothing,' said the Operations Chief.

The Commissar scratched his head. His eyes were shining. He spoke again:

'We wait for the mechanic on the path out of the village. He leaves for work early in the morning. We hand over the money and apologize . . .'

'Risky, very risky,' Fearless said, 'the roads must be patrolled.'

'Three men on their own can go anywhere without being spotted.'

'The mechanic tells the tuga, who must be watching the neighbourhood, and they cut off your retreat. You have to come along the Lombe and it is easy to cut . . .'

'It's not at all easy. Cut us off? Anyway, do you have a better idea?'

'I do,' Fearless said, 'drop it.'

'We can't.'

'Comrade Commissar,' Ops said, 'listen to comrade Commander, it is a dangerous plan. And the result . . .'

'That's where you're making a mistake. Risk must be measured against the importance of the matter. And you do not understand that this is basic, could determine the impression the people have of us. It is the most important of all.'

Fearless was smoking his first cigarette that day. He had one left, which would be kept for the next day. I am getting old, he thought, beginning to become provident. Once I would have smoked all the cigarettes at the beginning and then gone on suffering as long as was necessary. Only the old are able to ration pleasure. And it is because

41

of being old, at thirty five, that I tore a strip off Muatianvua for his audacity. And is it because of being old that I do not support the generous courage of the Commissar? Danger is like pleasure, the young cannot ration it.

'Who would you go with?' Fearless asked.

'Two volunteers. One would have to be Struggle, as the only one who knows the forest.'

'And us? Would we stay here and wait for you?'

'What for? We could meet at Base.'

'I'm still not in agreement, comrades,' the Operations Chief said. 'It's too dangerous. The tuga are alerted, they have informers all over the place. You will leave tracks, they will spot them. The people themselves will point out the tracks.'

The Commander interrupted:

'Leave it! We shall change the plan a little. One team of six will go as far as the tractor. Three will go on and three will wait. The others remain here. If anything happens, we will go to the rescue. The tuga are busy now burying the dead . . .'

'But we've almost nothing to eat,' Ops said.

'That's true, Commander,' the Commissar said. 'The best thing is to start for Base and leave us the food that's left. In two days' time we'll be at Base.'

'Okay,' Fearless said, 'we'll compromise. You three go. I and two more comrades will stay close to the village, to protect you if need arises. The others will return with Ops to Base. That's my decision!'

'But . . .' Ops said.

'That's my decision,' Fearless repeated.

'Why you, Commander?' the Commissar asked.

'And why you, Commissar?' said Fearless.

◆

The Operations Chief set out at seven for the Base. Fearless and two guerrillas followed with the Commissar, Struggle and New World. They advanced cautiously, avoiding tracks they encountered in the forest. At midday they neared a village: shouts and children's crying could be heard. They moved away again to prepare lunch.

42

In the afternoon, Struggle and New World went to carry out a reconnaissance. They returned to the others, three hours later.

'Any soldiers?' Fearless asked.

'We didn't go very close. We saw the path that leads to the road. We didn't go close, so as not to be seen or leave tracks.'

'Good. So let us three go ahead, to sleep by the path,' the Commissar said. 'You three stay here, Commander.'

'Yes, chief!' Fearless said. He gave a signal to the Commissar to come close and whispered in his ear:

'Ops has told me hundreds of times to be careful of Struggle.'

'Do you believe that?'

'Personally no. But I must mention it to you.'

'If you had gone, as I suggested, you would by now have been smoking all the cigarettes you wanted at Base. So, you're going to suffer for another night and day . . .'

'One must be able to defer pleasure . . . Then it tastes better.'

The guerrillas hugged, as they did before they went to face danger. Then, the Commissar, Struggle and New World set off, cautiously, along the path. They took an hour to arrive, with their concern to listen for sounds and to avoid breaking any dried sticks. At nightfall they settled ten metres from the path, and were invisible among the foliage and in the gloom. They snuggled among the lianas, covered themselves with the leafy branches, and prepared to spend the night there.

They were woken by the first voices that escaped the narrow confines of the village, and the dew that refreshed the green of the leaves. They shook off the numbness of limbs and of body pained by the roots on which they had been lying. In the dark they advanced to the path. They lay in ambush at the side. Every dog that barked made them feel like robbers awaiting a victim. But they were waiting for a man to hand him back his money. An odd situation to lead one to hide, thought New World. Only colonialism could cause such anomalies.

The voices came closer. Two men were chatting, as they strolled along. Impossible to see their faces, in the darkness. They could not stop them, to ask who they were. The men reached right in front of them and Struggle made out that they were talking about a battle. The Commissar squeezed an arm of each of his companions, indicat-

43

ing that they should do nothing. The men went by. Struggle whispered to the others that neither of the men was the mechanic.

'How do you know?'

'From his voice.'

Fifteen minutes later, a face showed in the near-total darkness. It was a woman going to the field. They let her pass.

It was already growing light, when they saw some ten metres away the intelligent face of the mechanic. He was coming with another worker, the old man with a crippled leg. As they passed close by, the Commissar called out softly:

'Malonda!'

The man addressed turned to them, astonished and frightened. Then Struggle emerged from the foliage with which he was camouflaged.

'It's us. Come here just a minute.'

The workmen recognized Struggle. They hesitated, looked backwards, in the direction of the village, then asked themselves a silent question. Struggle repeated the request and the men decided to enter the forest.

The guerrillas moved off with them a few steps from the path.

'We've brought you your money,' the Commissar said. 'One of our comrades had stolen it. He will be tried and punished. Here's your money.'

'Did you come just for that?' the cripple asked. 'It was risky . . .'

'It was our duty. MPLA defends the people, and does not steal from the people,' New World said.

'Better for you not to have come,' the mechanic said, 'it didn't matter.'

'It did matter,' the Commissar said. 'You might have believed we were bandits, as the Portuguese say, and that is not true.'

'But you can keep the money,' the mechanic said. 'Honest! I donate it to the MPLA. That's the truth, keep it.'

The mechanic was looking back nervously, towards the path. They were only whispering, but a whisper can carry a long way, in that forest. The Commissar expressed his thanks and held onto the money.

'Did you hear about the battle?'

'Yes,' the cripple said, with a smile. 'Lots died. A lad from the village over there died. There was a funeral yesterday.'

'We are always telling Angolans to desert from the army. Bullets don't choose,' the Commissar said. 'Was he the only Angolan to die?'

'No. There was another. But he was from the South. Lots of whites died. One was a captain.'

'What was his name?'

'Captain Lima. They gave orders for tracks to be looked for everywhere, but the people are not doing it . . .'

'What about you, did they do anything?'

'Questioning,' the mechanic said. 'Lots of questions. How many guerrillas were there, what was the chief like, where did they go, what did they say, what did they eat, what weapons did they have . . . They showed photographs, to see if you were the ones in the photos. Not one was! What really annoyed them was the mines. Said we knew about the mines and said nothing. But we didn't know. They are fine ones . . . Put a PIDE man there in the village.'

'Do you know who it is?'

'Yes we know. Why should he arrive just now? He's definitely PIDE. That's why it's dangerous here . . .'

'Yes, we're just going,' Struggle said.

Voices could be heard on the path. They waited for the steps to go away, then they bade farewell to the workmen. The latter made their way cautiously to the path, looked in both directions and, seeing no-one, joined it. The guerrillas had followed them, to see if they would in fact go on from the village or return. They waited for a few more minutes, with tense nerves, to check that the workers would not betray them. Reassured, they plunged into the wood.

When they reached the rendezvous, their comrades were already up.

'So?' Fearless asked.

'It all went well. We found him without difficulty. He gave us the money even. Donation to the MPLA!'

Fearless's hoot of laughter was imprudent, it could be heard a long way off. But the Commander could not contain himself.

'Really . . . to go so far, to run such a risk, and keep the money in your pocket . . .'

A shade testily, the Commissar replied:

'But it was what had to be done . . .'

'I know, I know. But it's still funny!'

They left in a hurry, trying to get away from the danger zone. Lunch was merely the remains of a tin of sardines, and cost them ten minutes. They continued the march, cutting a path without worrying about tracks they might leave. Night found them on the march, but they decided to go on anyway, as they were keen to sleep under a roof and to eat something hot.

The darkness and mud brought numerous falls. But for Struggle's sense of direction, they would have been lost a thousand times in the twists of the Lombe. Fatigue, pain, hunger had vanished, they were walking machines. But at ten at night they reached Base. They had walked for sixteen hours consecutively.

Before greeting anyone, Fearless asked for a cigarette. And he smoked it right through, leaning against a tree and listening to the Commissar telling the others what had happened. Only when he had finished the cigarette, and felt it burning his fingers, did Fearless remember that he still had his pack on his back. Then he went to heat water for coffee and to smoke another cigarette. For eating, he had the whole night . . .

◆

The trial of Ungrateful Tuga was held next day. In the trial all the guerrillas at Base took part. Ungrateful admitted that he had stolen. Each guerrilla spoke, all condemned the act. But some suggested extenuating circumstances; among them, Theory and Ekuikui. Then the Command met, to discuss the penalty.

The Commissar was first to speak:

'As the Disciplinary Law provides and as is customary in other Regions, there is only one punishment for this crime: firing squad. I have nothing more to say, the situation is clear. Ungrateful should be shot, for stealing goods from the people, for sabotaging relations between the Movement and the people, especially now that we are at the start.'

The Commissar's words were not followed by protestations. His hardness provoked a frozen silence and shiver in the other two. Only

46

after some time did the Operations Chief cease toying with his sheath-knife, to declare:

'I think comrade Commissar is being very harsh. We must not forget the attitude of these people against MPLA. Many comrades have already died, because of the people's treachery. That's why the guerrillas don't like the Cabinda people. This leads them to commit crimes. He was wrong, I know. No-one defends Ungrateful, but that must be borne in mind as well. A mistake is less serious, if there are previous factors that lead persons to make those mistakes.'

'That is no excuse! If the people were treacherous before, there were causes. They were not politicized, Taty deceived them and they believed that the tuga would change policy and that we were the ones in the way, because we insisted on waging war. And Ungrateful was told. How much time did we spend explaining how the people must be treated? Previous mistakes do not excuse a current mistake. And there is only one punishment. We are the ones who allow these mistakes that spoil our relations with the people. We are the ones, with our weakness, our tribalism, who prevent the exercise of discipline. Like this nothing will ever change.'

The Operations Chief was about to reply, when Fearless began to speak:

'Commissar, you are young, and, like all the young, unbending. But look at it calmly. What should be done with someone who steals money from the Movement? Firing squad. Has anyone been shot yet? No. What should happen to someone who, without reason, refuses to come to the Base? Expulsion, after a spell in prison, isn't it? But what happens to him in reality? He is spared, nothing worse happens than some fifteen days in prison and then he stays in Dolisie. I could give you more examples . . . How can we, now, apply the supreme penalty, the death penalty? It is not weakness, believe me. But the indiscipline that rules outside causes indiscipline here. The examples from outside, from abroad, from refugees dressed up as militants, have an effect on the fighters, weaken their morale. That would not happen if the Region were functioning well. Look at Ungrateful! A fighter in the North from '61 to '65. A fighter in Cabinda since that time. For ten years he has been fighting the enemy. Has he got little political training? Certainly. But it is not his fault. Whose is it? He sees the

47

examples from above. It is not your fault either. You take the deed as a personal affront, because you are Commissar, in charge of political training. You cannot do more than you do to convince Ungrateful that the Cabinda people are the same as the rest of Angola. Likewise Ungrateful cannot be convinced by mere words. Only practice will make him understand. It is not right to shoot a fighter with ten years of struggle, when other criminals go scot-free, even if in theory his crime merits that punishment. No, it cannot be done. In other circumstances, Ungrateful would not have done what he did and would have been receptive to the training we tried to give him. But in this context it is impossible.'

The Operations Chief gave his support:

'If we did execute him, either there would be a revolt or the majority of guerrillas would desert. And we don't have the manpower . . .'

'That is no argument,' the Commissar said. 'If only five remain, but five good ones, five conscious . . . that is better than having many, thanks to compromises. I cannot accept blackmail!'

'Blackmail?'

'Yes, that is blackmail. Poorly trained guerrillas use blackmail because of a shortage of manpower. The real manpower is there where we were, in those villages, in those industries. That is the real manpower in this Region. It is not by allowing theft we shall win this manpower. And people in charge accepting this blackmail!'

The tone had heightened perilously. So Fearless intervened:

'I think the Commissar is right in this regard. It is not an argument. But I would like him to respond to my arguments.'

'You are sentimental, Fearless!' the Commissar said, in changed tone. 'I do not believe you would have the courage even to order a traitor shot.'

Fearless clenched his hands, the knuckles of which had turned white. His lips quivered. He spoke softly, controlling himself with an effort:

'You should know comrade Commissar, that I have already executed a traitor. Not only did I take the decision, alone, but I also executed him, alone. And it was not with a shot, as the enemy were surrounding the place where we were. It was with a knife! Have you

48

ever stuck a knife into someone's belly, Commissar? Have you ever felt the knife bury itself in someone's belly? I could have avoided doing it, but everybody was being evasive, there were no volunteers, no-one had the courage, yes, no-one had the courage, to order a comrade to execute him, I chose myself as volunteer, to set an example. You were not here yet; if people don't talk about it, that is because nobody likes to talk about certain matters. On that occasion I did not run away from my duty, comrade. And it was the most difficult duty to take on, in comparison it is child's play to volunteer for an attack on a barracks ... There are murderers, who enjoy killing. For men who respect human life, who struggle because they respect human life, comrade, it is very difficult to volunteer to execute a man with a knife, even if he is a wretched traitor. I saw the faces of the others. The greatest fighters turned away so as not to see, the hardiest fighters covered their eyes with their hands. And these hands, comrade, these hands stuck the knife in the traitor's gut and tore his belly open, from top to bottom. And my whole body felt the death throes of the other man's body. Do you want more details? Comrade Commissar, I thank you for your words, which brought back to me a dreadful moment, the most dreadful ... Thank you, Commissar ...'

He choked and was silent. The Commissar saw in a flash the tears that blurred Fearless's eyes. Every whispered word had been like a slap. He said nothing, had nothing to say, there was nothing more to say.

'Anyway,' Ops said. 'We do not have the authority to condemn a guerrilla to death. We can make the proposal, but the decision lies with the leadership ...'

I, THE NARRATOR, AM MIRACLE.

See the injustice. I, Miracle, come from Quibaxe, where men attacked the enemy with only machetes and their courage, I come from far away, my father was killed, his head taken off by a tractor. To see one of ours, in cuffs, going off to the Congo, in cuffs, because he hung on to a hundred escudos of a Cabinda traitor! I, Miracle, should live to see this!

Ungrateful was sentenced to six months in prison. And how many traitors are not punished, are even accepted? Was Struggle punished? He tried to warn the workmen that we were going to capture them, tried to sabotage the mission, was he punished? And Ekuikui who kept the money instead of handing it over straightaway, was he punished? Only one of ours was.

Who decided? The Commander. Who pressed for his condemnation? The Commander, always the Commander. An intellectual, who knows nothing of life, who did not suffer, is he the man to condemn us?

That's how life goes on. Ah, in the First Region . . . In the First Region, it wouldn't be like this! This Commander would long ago have gone to the tuga, to escape our punishment. And the Commissar would follow, this kid who does only what Fearless tells him. Fearless? Who gave him that name? I never saw that he was so brave. He's brave, all right, but not exceptionally so.

This is the injustice we witnessed, without being able to do anything. When will it change? Oh, Nzambi, when will it change?

CHAPTER 2

Base

Mayombe had accepted the axe blows that opened up a clearing in it. A clearing invisible from above, from the aircraft that scoured the forest in an attempt to detect the presence of guerrillas. Huts had been put up in the clearing and the trees happily provided a vault of branches and leaves to cover them. Sticks served as walls. The roof grass was carried from far away, from the Lombe. A hillside was dug into to become an oven for the bread. The dead sticks of the walls put out roots and gripped the earth and the cabins became fortresses. And the men, dressed in green, turned green like the leaves and chestnut like the colossal trunks. The vault of foliage would not allow the sun to enter and the grass did not grow down below, on the clean space that linked the houses. Not linked: separated them with yellow, as the link was made by the green.

Thus was born of Mayombe the guerrilla base.

Food was scarce and the forest provided 'commons', dried fruit, huge almonds, whose shells were cut open with a knife and the fruit eaten raw or cooked. The 'commons' were food-stuff, contained oil and protein, provided energy, and hence were given the name 'commons'. The place where the fruits were stored and cooked was given the name 'Party Headquarters'. This 'communism' fattened the men, restored them from seven days of forced marches and exhausting emotions. Mayombe had made the fruit, but did not deign to show it to men: it left that to the apes, who scattered the split shells near the Base, with their tracks. And the guerrillas understood then that Mayombe-god was choosing this way of paying tribute to the courage of those who challenged him: Zeus humbled by Prometheus, Zeus concerned for Prometheus's safety, regretting having chained him, now sending the eagle, not to peck his liver, but to help him. (Was it Zeus who chained Prometheus, or the other way round?)

The forest made ropes at men's feet, made cobras in front of men, the forest generated impassable mountains, wild animals, storms,

51

foaming rivers, mud, darkness. Fear. The forest opened up pits camouflaged with leaves under the feet of men, immense noises in the silence of night, smashed trees down on men. And the men went on. The men turned green, and from their arms sprouted leaves, and flowers, and the forest curved into a vault, and the forest offered them its protective shade, and fruits. Zeus kneeled before Prometheus. And Prometheus with impunity gave fire to men, and intelligence. And men understood that Zeus was not after all invincible, that Zeus bowed to courage, thanks to Prometheus who gave them the intelligence and strength to assert themselves as men in opposition to the gods. Such is the attribute of a hero, to lead men to challenge the gods.

Such is Ogun, the African Prometheus.

◆

Three days after the mission, there arrived at the Base a group of eight guerrillas. They were all young, of ages varying between sixteen and twenty. They had recently in secrecy crossed the river Congo, from Kinshasa to Brazzaville, and undergone one month's military training.

'It's very little,' Fearless said. 'And this one here is too young, must do some more studying. He's just a kid! We need guerrillas, they send us untrained kids. Only useful as guards.'

'They can be trained here,' the Commissar said.

'And in the meantime? They'll cause us difficulties. Trying to increase manpower haphazardly, without regard to quality. There are others abroad, with enough experience, but as they are cousins of so and so in charge, they can't come into the guerrilla force. The ones without cousins have to put up with it . . .'

New World gave a mischievous smile and, winking at the Commissar, said:

'But, comrade Commander, the smallest one is from comrade Andre's family. He's from his own family, it seems.'

'I know,' Fearless said. 'But he is a cousin in disgrace, as his father smashed Andre's face in Kinshasa, in 1963, when they were UPA . . . Some story about medicines disappearing. On such matters between Kikongos I am well informed, as I too belong to the family . . .'

They were gathered in the Command hut, the evening assembly place, before listening to MPLA's radio broadcast. The young guerrilla candidate, who had just arrived, backed timidly into a corner. He had difficulty in understanding Portuguese, what he spoke was Kikongo and French, and the Commander's personality scared him: they were distantly related and he had heard much about him; now, he was meeting him for the first time. The bushy beard and unkempt hair of the Commander, his huge head, strong body, firm voice, sharp gaze, all combined to scare him. Fearless turned towards him.

'What is your nom de guerre?'

'I don't have one.'

'Fine. We must pick a name. What do you suggest, comrades?'

The guerrillas studied the boy. He lowered his eyes.

'Onkoka, cobra,' Ekuikui suggested.

'Leave off your Umbundu,' Fearless cut in. 'Either give him a name in his language, or in Portuguese, which all of us have. But not in yours . . . That's the beginning of Umbundu imperialism! Anyway, he doesn't give me any impression of a cobra.'

The baptism of a guerrilla was always a subject for lengthy discussions. Suggestions came from all sides. The guerrillas made him stand in the middle of the hut, so as to study his characteristics and find a suitable name. Roars of laughter accompanied the words. Each told an anecdote he knew about him, until a clear picture was drawn of the new recruit. The other seven arrivals awaited their turn. Miracle suggested 'Advance' and straightaway Mautianvua said this was wrong, he had more the appearance of someone in retreat. Amid the laughter and jokes, they agreed on one characteristic: timidity. Finally they were unanimous in the nickname of VW, the tortoise*.

'Good, VW, you're one of us,' Fearless said. 'I hope you will not give us too much trouble, especially to the Commissar here. Washing your nappies . . .'

'You're being hard on him,' the Commissar whispered.

'So that he shouldn't think being a relative of mine gives him any privileges. Which does not necessarily mean that I will be a bad hen to this chick . . .'

* VW is the name given to the Volkswagen car (V.W.). The guerrillas used the name as a synonym for tortoise because of the similarity of shape. (Author's note).

They baptised the other newcomers and listened to the broadcast. When the senior men remained alone in the Command hut, Fearless said:

'They send us more mouths and do not send food. Commissar, you will have to go out there to find food. Unless one of us goes, we could very well die of hunger, since the civilians abroad are not bothered. That's how this war is!'

The Operations Chief was frustrated, because he wanted to go to Dolisie to spend a few days with his wife. He merely threw a loaded look at the Commissar.

'You should be the one to go, Commander,' the Commissar said. 'You haven't been out of here for three months. Since the Base has been inside . . . A week outside would do you good.'

'I find you a joke! You are keen to go for reasons we all know . . . You know very well that the civilians annoy me, that I cannot stand being in Dolisie. And you have the cheek to tell me that a week outside would do me good! For a start, if I were to go, I would smash the face of my cousin Andre, who sends us these wet-nappies and no food. Better that you go, who respect Andre, as your senior . . .'

'A matter of discipline!'

'You hang on to those feelings! That's why my choice is right.'

'But perhaps Ops would like to go,' the Commissar suggested.

The Operations Chief shrugged his shoulders, although anxious for Fearless's response. It sounded like a whiplash in the forest:

'Pas question! Whoever it is has to take Ungrateful to prison. Ops would be capable of letting him run away, just because he is a relative.'

Ops shrank at the whiplash sound. He gave a half-smile, a smirk glued to his lips.

'But, comrade Commander, you're joking . . . I . . .'

'Joking? I was never more serious in my life. Do you think I don't know my people?'

The Commissar was delighted with the reply. Ops would not dare to react to the reference, he was a carpet under the Commander's feet. The gall must be choking him, but he maintained the servile attitude of a beaten dog. Moments later, the Commissar rebuked himself for rejoicing in what was going on: to make amends, he ended the discussion swiftly.

'All right, I will go then ... I don't mind, after all. Since there is food here for three days only, as soon as I find something, I'll make Andre send a resupply group. I leave tomorrow, then. What other matters are there to be settled there? Our strength is now thirty guerrillas, a higher monthly budget has to be allocated. A new medic must be found, to replace Pangu-Akitina for a few days, as he must go to Pointe-Noire for eye treatment ...'

'Agreed, agreed,' Fearless interrupted. 'Don't machine gun any more; you're like a woman I knew who fired two hundred words a minute. You are a Jesus Christ, you and your notion of honour: you don't want Judas to be punished in front of you, although you know that he betrayed you with his kiss. It's not worth the bother, I'm not going on.'

The Operations Chief did not follow, but the Commissar did: Fearless had read all his thoughts and, mercifully, did not want to wound his scruples further.

The Commissar looked at Fearless in astonishment, as someone stares at a magician, and the commander smiled:

'It's not by chance that I am thirty-five, youngster!'

◆

The Commissar left in the morning with a small group, including Ungrateful Tuga. After the group's departure, most of the guerrillas went to the room at the centre of the Base that was used as a school. Three fighters went out on patrol, others were busy cooking, some did nothing, finding excuses to avoid study.

The Commander went with the new recruits to a clearing, put them through exercises and explained the rudiments of guerrilla war. The Operations Chief went hunting with a .22. New World, who had studied in Europe, sometimes helped Theory. But he was free that day, and accompanied the group of novices. Stretched out on the grass, where the rare Mayombe sun shone for two hours, he cleaned his weapon and listened absent-mindedly to Fearless's explanations.

Struggle had already gone by once towards the river and returned to the Base. He came back on his way to the river, watched the group for a while, and ended up sitting beside New World.

'Go to school!'

'Oh! I've work to do,' Struggle said.

'What have you got to do?'

'Wash clothes . . .'

New World smiled. Struggle was a habitual truant from school, especially when the Commissar was not around. He had already been punished for not studying, but had not changed.

'You must convince yourself that you need to study. What use will you be after the struggle? If you can't read . . . where will you work?'

'Stay in the army,' Struggle said.

'And do you think that you don't have to study to stay in the army? How are you going to learn about artillery or military tactics or armoured cars? You need mathematics, physics . . .'

'Hang on! I don't want to be an officer.'

'So who will be an officer, then? Those trained in the tuga army, without political training, who will attempt a coup d'etat one day? Is that what you want? That after independence there should be coups d'etat every year, like in the other African countries? We must have a highly politicized army, with cadres from the liberation struggle. What are we going to do, if the guerrillas don't want to study to become cadres?'

Struggle shrugged his shoulders. He gazed at the group of young men who were somersaulting on the ground, sweating, with sweat clinging to the Mayombe mud, and the Commander, bare-chested, somersaulting as well, standing up then rolling on the ground, mixing instruction with encouragements and shouts.

'Comrade New World, there are lots who do study. One person who does not want to study is not going to ruin everything. I was born in the forest, what I like is hunting, to go from one place to another, to make war. But I don't like to study at all. I've put up with it, learned to read and write. I can even do my multiplication tables! For me that's enough. The Commissar mobilized me, last year I studied. But now that's enough, the Commissar won't be able to mobilize me any more. What you said is the truth, is right. But the people's militias will prevent coups d'etat, the people in arms . . .'

'And who's going to teach the people? It is us. Who is going to incorporate the militias? There must be a well-trained army. So experienced cadres are needed.'

'That's what comrade Commissar says. All those with lots of politics in their head talk like that. But I don't have a lot of politics in my head, I'm just a guerrilla. When independence comes, if they don't want me in the army, I'll come back here, turn hunter in Mayombe. I don't want to be much. There are some who want to be directors, chiefs of I don't know what, commanders . . . Let them study. I don't want to be a chief.'

New World finished cleaning his weapon. He began to assemble it carefully. Struggle, with his Pepesha between his knees, observed the operation.

'There are comrades who study merely to climb, that's true. But you can't say this of all. There are others who really want to be useful, or who want to learn for the pleasure of learning.'

'Tsk!' Struggle said. 'I don't believe it. All of them want to climb or to live better or to give orders.'

'Not all, not all. Sure a person who improves himself is thinking about his personal future as well, reckons that he can have a better life. But there are some who think of this alone and others who think more of the good of the people.'

'Name me one here in the Base, one who is like that . . .'

'They're to be found.'

'Name one!'

'I don't know. I don't know them well, I've just come. But I think there are, must think there are . . .'

Fearless had interrupted the exercises for a short rest. He had heard the last remarks. He sat down by them and asked:

'Must think there are, New World? Must think?'

New World stroked his thin beard. He hesitated for some moments.

'Yes, I must think.'

'Like believers who feel they must believe in god? Because they are afraid of giving up belief, of losing the protection of this belief which gives meaning to their life, is that it?'

'It's not quite that.'

'It's almost that. It's practically the same thing. When anyone

57

declares that he must believe in the unselfishness of some men, because that corresponds to the idea he has of mankind, even though the facts show the opposite, what is that then? He has a preconceived notion of the human race, an optimistic concept. Therefore, he denies any reality that contradicts the concept. This is schematism in politics. It is a religious aspect, a religious conception of politics. Unfortunately it is the way many revolutionaries do think.'

'But, comrade Commander, don't you think there are comrades who study unselfishly?'

'Do you believe anything in life is done unselfishly?'

Struggle thought that he had found support from the Commander. He felt the courage to offer:

'That is why I don't agree with the Commissar, who makes us go to school.'

'You, Struggle, are an ass!' Fearless said. 'Anyone who does not want to study is an ass and, therefore, the Commissar is right. Do you want to go on being a dummy, cheated by everybody . . . People must study, as it is the only way they can think things out with their own head and not with the head of others. Man must know much, ever more and more, to win his freedom, to be able to form judgements. If you don't understand the words I utter, how can you know if I'm speaking soundly or not? You have to ask someone else. You're always dependent on someone else, you are not free. So everyone must study, the principal aim of a genuine Revolution is to make everyone study. But comrade New World here is an innocent, since he believes there are some who study merely for the good of the people. It is this blindness, this idealism that causes the worst mistakes. There is nothing unselfish.'

'You are training these youngsters. What do you gain personally by that?'

Fearless lit a cigarette, and stretched out on the grass.

'I could tell you I feel sorry for them, so poorly trained and in danger of dying soon in the first battle. There could be some truth in that. Likewise I could tell you it is to train more guerrillas, for the struggle to advance. That's it! But why do I want the struggle to advance? Isn't it just to live better in an independent Angola? So, what I am doing has a selfish purpose, which is natural and human.

Likewise I could tell you it is to strike a blow at the civilians in Dolisie, who send us men with insufficient training. That might be true too. So? Tell me where is the unselfishness?'

New World weighed the words. The recruits were coming near, seeing the Commander smoking. Fearless ordered them to go on with the exercises and observed them.

'But don't you think, Commander, that there could be totally unselfish men?'

'Jesus Christ? . . . I think so, there are some rare ones. But they are not always so. The Commissar, for example, is to some extent unselfish. I think he could match up to some of the elect, at a certain period. But it is temporary. No-one is permanently unselfish.'

'Not Lenin?'

'Lenin! I didn't know Lenin, how can I talk about him? Talk about those I know, men I knew. I must tell you that I never saw anyone totally and permanently unselfish. And don't drag great men into the discussion, just to scare the rest and strengthen your case. That is a politician's trick!'

'I believe there are men for whom the good of others is all that matters. Che Guevara, Henda, to name just two examples. And many others, anonymous. Anyone who does not believe this has no confidence in human generosity, in mankind's capacity for sacrifice. He is a pessimist . . .'

'And, therefore, incapable of struggling coherently, isn't that it?' Fearless said.

New World looked straight at him. He lowered his head, murmured:

'That's it.'

New World's eyes quickly brightened and he went on more strongly:

'To struggle in a coherent manner requires a minimum of optimism, of confidence in men. I am thinking of me, and you are thinking of yourself, Commander! I am confident. If you were not an optimist, you could not fight.'

'What do I do?'

'I don't deny that you fight, no. But you might give up, if the difficulties were great, you could tire more easily than someone else more optimistic. A profound faith is needed, to put up with everything all the time.'

You have just come, just joined the guerrilla war, Fearless thought. What right do you have to talk as if you had already stood up to innumerable vicissitudes? You have not even seen the real war, but you are already saying that you would be more resistant than I. All these young men come from Europe with the idea that theoretical study of Marxism is a magic potion that will make them perfect in practice. However, he is a man to speak up in front of his Commander, which is a good start; the rest will come later perhaps, in time, with the buffeting he will take in life.

'I think it is like religion,' Fearless said. 'There are some who need it. There are some who need to believe in an abstract generosity of abstract mankind, to be able to follow a road as hard as the revolutionary road. I regard them as weak or as young spirits, who have not yet really seen life. The weak give up merely because their ideal has fallen down, on seeing a leader cheat a militant. The others mature, become more relative, less demanding. Or they keep their faith alight. They die happy, although perhaps uselessly. But there are men who do not need faith to make sacrifices; they are the ones who, rationally, in complete independence, choose this road, knowing that the target will be only half achieved, but that this means immense progress. Clearly they too have an ideal, everyone has, but in them the ideal is not abstract or unreal. I know, for example, that we all have deep inside us an egotistic streak that we try to hide. That is how man is, at least existent man. What is the effect of centuries and millennia of individual economy, except to make men egotistic? To deny it is to dodge the hard, but real truth. In short, I know that actual man is egotistic. Therefore, one must always show him that the little achieved is insufficient and that he must persevere. Does this prevent me going on? Why? If I know this, in cold blood, and even so decide to struggle, if I try to help these small egotists against the big egotists who hoard everything, then I do not see why I should have to give up when others go on. I shall stop only, and rationally, when I see that my action is useless, that it is gratuitous, namely if the Revolution were diverted from its basic aims.'

Struggle had given up following the discussion and gone off to the

60

riverside. The new guerrillas had given up their somersaults and were waiting for the Commander. New World, lost in thought, did not respond. Standing up, Fearless said:

'Don't you agree? You don't have to. But let's talk again, when we have more time. Now I have to take care of my chicks!'

He merged in among them, while New World obstinately followed with his eyes the creepers that climbed the trees, only to fall again to the side, weaving the Mayombe-god into an enormous, interlaced web, which shackled him and gave him being.

I, THE NARRATOR, AM NEW WORLD.

I refuse to believe what Fearless says. There he is, over there, among the youngsters, scraping himself on the forest roots, crawling, bashing his shoulders on the hard, rotten, damp soil of Mayombe, making himself hoarse with shouts and curses, losing his virility in the seed of the forest, in the generative seed of the giants, sweating the dirt of the tree bark, nipping himself on the fruit hidden beneath the fallen leaves, there he is, over there among the youngsters, teaching what he knows, unreservedly, giving himself to his pupils, opening himself like the strong thighs of a virgin, and he, over there, says that he is acting selfishly.

Fearless is unselfish, he gave his spare shirt to the guide, who ran off with it and gave himself up to the tuga.

If he says that he is selfish, that is vanity. It is the vanity of revealing what many hide, it is a declaration of character. Clearly it is an exaggerated, extremist declaration, a fault of his petty bourgeois mentality.

As if it were possible to make a Revolution only with selfish men, egotists! I am not egotistic, Marxism-Leninism showed me that man as an individual is nothing, only the masses can make History. If I were egotistic, I would be in Europe now, like so many others, working and earning good money. Why did I come to struggle? Because I am unselfish. Workers and peasants are unselfish, they are the people's vanguard, a pure vanguard, that does not bear the original sin of the bourgeoisie, from which intellectuals can free themselves only with great difficulty. I freed myself, thanks to Marxism.

So Fearless is mistaken. But how to explain to him, make him understand that his anarchist attitude is damaging the struggle? There he is, and he laughs when one of them is hurt, and he is angry when one hesitates, and it is this maternal sadism that makes them extend themselves, overcome fear and throw themselves into space to grab a flimsy creeper. And a triumphant smile flashes in his eyes, a discreet smile that is quickly lost in the order given to the next. But, how remorsefully he would twist in bed if a recruit were seriously injured! Seeing him, one would say he has no soul. But he was the one to expose himself to save Muatianvua, when they fell in an ambush, and who wept with relief at finding him unhurt. How can it be said that everyone is egotistic? It is vanity, petty bourgeois vanity, and nothing more.

I cannot believe, I refuse to believe.

The Commissar ran all over the place, in Dolisie, hunting for Andre who was in charge.

The latter had given him an appointment for the previous afternoon, in a bar, and had not shown up. On the following morning, the Commissar was at Andre's house at seven, but the latter had already vanished. The Commissar instructed Truth to stay at the office, to wait, and he set off, looking into bars, touring the streets, popping into militants' houses. No trace of Andre.

I could have gone to see Ondine, since I arrived I have not even looked for her, and I am chasing after a fellow who hides from me! And he is supposed to be in charge? And Ondine must be furious that I have not shown up.

He went back to the office at eleven. Truth was keeping guard.

'He hasn't come in or gone out.'

'Stay here. I'm going to the school.'

The Commissar set off for the Movement's school (where Ondine taught), about a kilometre from the edge of town. The comrades at Base must be practically out of food, he thought. Blind anger gradually suffused him.

The excursion in the burning sun angered him further. He was not used to the sun, as he was always hidden in the protective shade of Mayombe. Ungrateful had gone to prison, but he had to inform

Andre of the Command's decision and sort out with him what routine Ungrateful should follow. And Andre was in hiding . . .

The school was on a slope, hidden by a clump of trees. The various adobe huts were spread over a radius of fifty metres, providing a school and hospital. Higher up were stick and mud huts, for the boarding houses.

The children were in class. Ondine too. He waited for her, greeting passers-by, asking about Andre. Meanwhile, Ondine had been informed that he had arrived and she came out of the classroom.

'You came yesterday, I know.'

'Yes. But I was chasing after comrade Andre. He's not to be found.'

Ondine was sulking, it was clear. He tried to take her hand, but she dodged, looking back.

'What's the matter?' he said. 'Everyone knows we're engaged . . .'

'Better not. Wait a bit, I'm just finishing the lesson. Are you coming to lunch with me?'

The Commissar hesitated, turned his eyes away.

'I must see if I can get hold of comrade Andre at lunch-time.'

'You mean you're going back to Dolisie already?' she asked coldly.

His comrades were hungry, that is why he had come, and for Ungrateful. He had not come for Ondine. With an effort he replied:

'I must go back soon. We have no food at Base . . .'

Ondine did not respond. She turned her back on him and went to the classroom. The Commissar stayed watching her, his guerrilla cap going from one hand to the other, her name stuck in his throat. He went to visit his wounded comrades, killing time, effacing her behaviour. He was the one who felt guilty.

The bell finally rang and Ondine came out, surrounded by the din of the children released. The Commissar went with her to her room. Ondine lived in a room of the only cement building, in a room she shared with a senior student, Yvonne.

'Why aren't you going to Dolisie?' she asked brusquely, when they reached the room.

'It's early still. Andre won't be there until one.'

He waited for her invitation and then sat on the bed. Ondine remained standing, pretending to arrange things, controlling her anger.

63

'Ondine, you must understand that I came to deal with certain urgent business . . . Yesterday night, I was about to come here, when I gave up hope of finding Andre . . . But it was late . . . You know how people talk, I preferred not to come . . .'

'What you preferred I know! You went to a bar . . .'

'But I was there only half an hour . . .'

He wanted to say that he was invited by a comrade. He wanted to explain to her what it meant to drink a cold beer when one had been months and months in the forest. He wanted to explain to her that he had paid no heed to the conversation, with wanting to come and see her, that she was reflected in the froth on the beer, that but for scandal-mongers . . . But he said nothing, abashed and overcome.

'They came and told me they'd seen you in the bar,' she said. 'Don't give me stories that you were chasing after Andre. Andre doesn't go to bars.'

'Doesn't go to bars? Spends his life in them!'

'What have you got against Andre? He wouldn't stay in the bar if he were in your situation.'

'Look, you don't want to understand.'

Ondine had come from Angola a year before. She had studied a good part of secondary school, more than he. Even after they became engaged, this was always a barrier. The Commissar considered that Ondine was doing him a favour, in accepting him, since she could aim for a more cultivated personality. He had instructed her politically, but even this did not convince him they were on an equal footing. If he did not drop these complexes, their love would fail, Fearless had said one day. But the Commissar had never had a sweetheart, his prior experience was exclusively with prostitutes, and this was a big disadvantage in regard to an Ondine who had already known other men.

The first time they made love was provoked by her, who took command, while he fretted, was scared, was inhibited. The impression that love-making was better with a tart was difficult to relinquish, even after several experiences with Ondine. Fearless was right, he should have confidence in himself. But he did not have it. And he felt that Ondine did not enjoy his style of love-making.

'I'll go and find him now. Early in the afternoon we can be together,

I'll come here. If food can be found, I'll send a group there and stay for a few days. It's the best I can do . . . We had a battle . . .'

The reminder made her jump. She turned to him and grabbed him by the hand.

'Yes, so I heard. It wasn't dangerous?'

'No, went off all right.'

They drew close. Her eyes shone. The Commissar felt an indefinable warmth climb his body and all the bitterness vanished. They kissed. I am forgiven, he thought. But he was already imagining how he would apologize next for going and the chill that would again come between them. His voice came out sadly:

'Ondine, I must go.'

'Go!'

He stood stock-still, cap in hand, eyeing the door and Ondine, Ondine and the door, indecisively. His comrades were hungry . . .

'I'll soon be back.'

And he went away, with a sob bursting out, and all his anger directed at Andre, who made him run after him, live for him, him, as the man with the food money. He shot off to the town, without speaking to anyone, taking revenge on the stones on the way, almost flying over the dusty road, under the merciless sun.

Andre arrived soon after him. Tall, skinny, with a thin goatee sharpening his face, an air of intellectual-aristocrat, such was Andre. He grasped the Commissar's arm, steered him to the veranda, saying softly:

'There are some serious problems with the Congolese, do you realize, comrade Commissar? That's why I'm rushing here and there. But I didn't forget about you. I'm beating my brains, there's no money . . . It's true, there's no money. But we'll fix something this afternoon, for sure. You're lunching with me, aren't you?'

The Commissar wanted to object, to say that he had seen the jeep going all over the place, for that there was money, that they were dying of hunger at the Base, that he was lying to him. But he was accustomed to showing respect for has seniors.

'There isn't a scrap of food at Base. Yesterday I was waiting for you . . .'

'Exactly, that's the problem I was telling you about. They came to call me urgently. But this afternoon we'll fix something, tomorrow you can go back to the Base.'

'I wanted to discuss other business with you. The case of Ungrateful . . .'

'Ah, yes, yes, quite right. Better for you to stay a few days in Dolisie.' He put his hand in his pocket and handed over a 500 franc note. 'To have a beer with comrade Ondine. Let's first go to lunch, some Congolese have given me a chicken.'

The Commissar did not want to accept the money, but Andre insisted. He kept it with the feeling that he was being bought: it was the price of his understanding. To refuse, to speak to Andre clearly and plainly, that was what Fearless would do. Or perhaps he would accept and still speak to him clearly and plainly. But Fearless was almost the same age as Andre, he not.

They sat down at the table and soon five more people came and sat and then Andre's wife. It was a stew from the chicken provided by the Congolese, according to what Andre had said. The chicken tasted off to the Commissar, tasted to him of the Movement's money. But he ate. His rage was all bottled up inside, rage against Andre, but, above all against himself. How easy it is to face the enemy! A thousand times easier than some political difficulties. Plunged into private spite, he restricted himself to monosyllabic mumbling in reply to Andre's questions. The latter gave up making him talk.

When lunch was over, the Commissar tried to discuss with Andre. But the latter sent him away.

'I'm just going to deal with food for the Base. Are there comrades to carry it?'

'Only three of us came. Not enough.'

'Okay, so I'll organize a resupply group. As soon as I find the money . . .'

'They must leave tonight,' the Commissar said.

'Yes, yes. When shall we meet? Here at six, is that all right?'

'All right,' the Commissar said, in frustration. Once again it was going to interfere with meeting Ondine.

Andre disappeared and the Commissar set off on the route to the school. He bumped into Truth, who was escorting a woman.

'Prepare to leave tonight. A resupply group is going.'

66

'But, comrade Commissar, I have some difficulty . . .'

'You leave tonight! Be ready!'

Truth was silent and went on his way. He is angry, the Commissar thought. His difficulty was that woman, with whom he wanted to spend the night obviously. But he still has time, departure is always at dawn. What right have I to stay here a few more days and send Truth back to Base? I am sending him, because they are under strength there, because he came on a mission he has already completed. So, he has no reason to stay. What about me? Why am I staying? Tonight I can perfectly well sort out with Andre what to do about Ungrateful. I have no other reason except Ondine. What right have I to send Truth back to Base, if, for the same reason, I am not going?

The doubt grew as he drew nearer the school. The ones in charge formed a caste that demanded all the privileges, the militants used to say. And it was true. It was true, and there he was proving it. The decision was already taken when he arrived at the school.

Ondine received him at first with hostility. But Yvonne then left the room and she became more tender. They went out arm-in-arm and went to lie in the grass, as far as possible from the school. They stopped below a magnificent mango tree, in whose shade they sat.

They made love once, twice, he still unskilfully. The Commissar was convinced that she was finding no pleasure and lost himself in distractions, searching for her reactions, without really relaxing or enjoying himself. She felt herself being spied on and stopped feeling enjoyment: the orgasm was the mechanical outcome of an automatic act. Afterwards they lied to each other, saying that they had found keen pleasure. Each knew that the other was lying. Ondine did not dare speak about the matter, since her fiance would be shocked: he did not permit the forming of the genuine intimacy of lovers who can talk naturally, without inhibition. They were an engaged couple, not lovers. And she was disturbed by the need for an explanation. She had decided to follow a practical course: in time he would relax and surrender himself. But time seemed incapable of solving the problem, as they saw each other infrequently; they met for two or three days, every couple of months, or worse. Only in marriage. Ondine knew, however, that marriage would not bring any change in their life, as he would remain at the Base and she at the school. There was a refusal to admit that they were at an impasse.

Deep inside herself, Ondine had nostalgia for other experiences, where she had found more pleasure. Would it always be like this with him? It was when they separated that she really felt an intense desire that had remained unfulfilled. Ondine refused to face up to this reality. She therefore steered their relations onto the intellectual plane.

'What's up with Andre? Seems you don't like him.'

'He's a saboteur! There's starvation at the Base, he sent a few young guerrillas, practically untrained, and didn't send food. I come to sort the matter out and he plays tricks on me. Makes appointments he does not keep, then says there is no money and that he is going to look for loans. But he gave me 500 francs, without my asking, and the jeep goes all over the place wasting petrol . . .'

'You're all the same! He gave you 500 francs and you're still complaining? If he hadn't given you, that's because he only gives to civilians and doesn't care about the guerrillas . . . Always finding something to criticize!'

'It's not that, Ondine. When there's no money to buy food for the Base, he has no business giving 500 francs for beer. If there is money, it is natural for him to give, a person who is in Mayombe for three months needs a little cash. But it depends on the situation and prospects . . .'

'Well I think Andre is a good official. He's always concerned about the needs of militants . . .'

'Not true,' the Commissar interrupted. 'He's concerned about certain persons, not about the militants.'

'He's never kept me short.'

'For you! But what about the rest?'

Ondine gave a gale of laughter. Pinching the Commissar's arm, she said:

'I've just realized. You don't like Andre because he always treats me well. You're jealous of him . . .'

'I?'

The young man's startled eyes soon convinced Ondine that she had completely missed the mark.

'I've never even thought about it . . . That he should be after you,

68

honestly never entered my head. But, basically, perhaps you are right. He's a scoundrel, has a pile of women over there, so they say. Perhaps he is after you. There aren't many here like you, educated, pretty . . .'

'Leave off! People talk too much. I've seen how he looks after his wife, not like a man who has other women. Slanders.'

'Well, he looks after her as the mother of his children . . .'

Ondine caressed him to take the frown from the Commissar's forehead. He went on:

'He has support among the women, they say he's a fine man. He's a good talker, gives the impression of better education than in reality . . . And he has an important post. In brief, things that count for an unpoliticized woman.'

'Not for all of them, even the unpoliticized. But forget Andre! Tell me about the battle.'

The Commissar complied, recounting what had happened. He included even the incident of Ungrateful and the Commander's response to his unfortunate remark about traitors.

'Fearless was right, seems to me,' Ondine said. 'And he was angry, because it came from you. You should hear how he talks about you, as if you were his son . . .'

'Yes, he likes me.'

They were silent, both thinking about Fearless. And the Commissar's anxiety returned. What am I going to say? How am I going to say that at six I must go to Dolisie and that, tonight, I leave? Especially as this morning I promised to stay for a few days . . .

His silence alerted Ondine. She studied him and spotted the frown in his forehead.

'What's the matter?'

'Nothing.'

'Tell your little Dina!'

He breathed deeply, plucking up courage.

'Do you know? At six I have a meeting, another one, with Andre. I'm going back tonight.'

She reared in a rage.

'But you said . . .'

'Yes, but Andre . . . Well, it wasn't Andre. I'm the one who thinks I must go. I've nothing to do here.'

Ondine did not reply. She remained seated, her arms on her knees, her skirt covering half her thighs.

'What about me?' she said.

The Commissar stroked her hair again.

'What about me?' she repeated.

'I will try to come as soon as possible.'

'Heavens!'

His caresses became more insistent and she felt her belly open to him in warmth. For some moments she forgot her irritation and yielded. But he was thinking of the imminent separation. It was already five, and he did not match her desire. He was once more detached and reasonable. Her fire eventually went out too soon and, when she had recovered her mood, he had already finished. Ondine's belly ached with dissatisfaction, as she returned to school. But she hid her ache and resentment. He was going to the battle front, a fighter's farewell cannot be made with complaints or scolding, only with tenderness, when there is some to offer.

The Commissar had to wait till eight o'clock, to catch sight of Andre. The latter arrived in a jeep with ten kilos of maize meal and as many again of rice and a little dried fish.

'It's what I could manage. I've assigned three comrades to carry this.'

'Only this? But this won't last two days even . . . And to carry this doesn't need three persons.'

'There's no money, comrade. This is what a Congolese gave me just now . . . Tomorrow I'll see if I can find more. And it's always good for the comrades from here to go to the Base. Even if one could carry this load, it's still good. Tomorrow there'll be more . . .'

Good for the comrades to go, but you have never set foot in the Base, the Commissar thought.

'Tomorrow . . .'

Andre clapped him on the arm.

'Had dinner yet?'

'I, no!'

'So come along . . . Tomorrow I'll find food for fifteen days.'

'I have to get ready for the journey. We must talk now, comrade Andre.'

'But tomorrow . . .'

'Today, right now! I start tonight.'

'But why? You could stay here another day or so and take the rest of the food . . .'

The Commissar wanted nothing but to escape Dolisie and take refuge at the Base. Here he would lose all his moral strength, and become demoralized.

'No! I must leave tonight. Let us talk. Dine later!'

'But . . .'

'Dine later!' the Commissar shouted. 'There are matters of war to deal with, dinner can wait. I am fed up with waiting for tomorrow.'

'All right, all right, comrade Commissar.'

The discussion took ten minutes, since Andre took note of what the Commissar said and agreed systematically. Andre was always in agreement with his interlocutor, it was his nature. Only in the case of Pangu-Akitina did he have to wait for a reply from Brazzaville, since there was no medical orderly available in Dolisie to replace him for a while at the Base.

When the meeting was over, the official invited the other for dinner.

'I've already had chicken for lunch, comrade Andre. I don't know if the comrades at the Base had any more for lunch than wild nuts. I do not need dinner. Till the next time, comrade Andre. And thank you for the 500 francs, I'm going to use them to buy food for the guerrillas.'

And he went out, slamming the door. It was open warfare, the Commissar knew that he had made another enemy.

At four in the morning, when they were preparing to leave, the Commissar asked the others:

'Where's Truth?'

'Not going.'

'Not going? How?'

'Has permission from comrade Andre to stay.'

'What? What? What?'

The Commissar ran about the dark room, banging the heels of his boots on the beaten earth. What? He felt an urge to go and drag Andre from bed and beat him. Who was Commissar at the Base? What right had Andre to stick his oar in the granting of permissions?

71

He was leaving so as not to set an example of abuse and the man in charge was encouraging abuses.

Almost with tears in his eyes he gave the order for departure. The cortege of five men went into the forest, at night, at a quick pace, whose rhythm was determined by a Commissar, in flight, like a madman, escaping despair, rushing to his Base, where things were normal, where men did what they could to struggle and to forget the climate that prevailed behind them. Day broke and the Commissar did not stop. At the head of the group, against all the security rules, he flew along the slippery trail, heedless of the pleas from the men who wanted to drink water, heedless of the lianas that struck him in the face, cheated, assaulted, swearing vengeance, seeking the company and assurance of Fearless, who was no longer disillusioned by anything, since he had no illusions.

And the journey took only five and a half hours, when usually it was exactly eight.

When he heard the Commissar's tale, Fearless laughed at him. He looked at his expression, half ashamed, half hurt, and he laughed, laughed till he curled up. The Operations Chief managed a light grin, which clung to his well-cultivated moustache.

'That's the result of being more papist than the Pope! You had every right to spend some days in Dolisie, as it's months since you were there and there was no urgent task here. You wanted to be blameless to the last, wanted to have a superior idea of yourself . . . You were caught! That's the result of being ingenuous. And do you think we'll receive food tomorrow? My foot! Another one of us is going to have to go there. But for the "commons", we would die of hunger.'

The Operations Chief raised an arm, as if asking permission to speak. He spoke deliberately, seeking with every word to cast a stone at the Commissar.

'Die of hunger, no, since I managed to hunt some wild-fowl. There's meat for a few days. And tomorrow perhaps I'll hunt more. It's a pity the Commissar forgot to bring more oil and salt, to use with the meat.'

The Commissar was about to retort.

'You did very well, Ops,' Fearless said. 'It was a brilliant operation! Let's appoint you official hunter for the Base.'

The Commander then turned to the Commissar.

'How was Ungrateful left?'

'I spoke to Andre. Everything settled. He stays in the Dolisie prison. Andre said that he would take special precautions . . .'

'I can imagine!' Fearless said.

The Commissar stood up and picked up his clean uniform.

'I'm going for a bath.'

'I'll go with you,' Fearless said.

They went to the river. Fearless stood guard, while the Commissar was washing. Coming out of the cold water, the Commissar ran for the clearing, taking advantage of the last rays of the sun. The Commander brought the shirt that he had forgotten by the river. He chucked it onto the grass. The Commissar sensed friendly solicitude in the gesture. This made him forget Fearless's contortions of laughter, when he had been relating to him the distasteful events in Dolisie.

'Between Ondine and me . . . things are not going well.'

Fearless's silence, as he sat smoking astride a fallen tree-trunk, encouraged him to say what had happened the day before. The Commander listened, with his eyes fixed on the muzzle of his AK.

'Sexually you two don't get on, isn't that it?'

'Why do you say that?' The Commissar threw him a worried glance, then went on:

'In the beginning no, but now things have become normal.'

Fearless threw away his cigarette. A pair of monkeys chased it in the nearest trees. A shot would have done for one of them, for sure. But the Commander did not dare break up the couple who were preparing to make love. One less meal, he thought. He turned his mind back to the conversation.

'I don't know. There is something that disturbs me, when I see you together. You make two persons, always two persons, not a symbiosis. It is as if you were constantly on watch, a kind of challenge between the two of you, using third parties in your duel. Love is a duel. But love achieved is also a sharing, they even say that old married people end up looking alike. You have not yet melted into one another,

73

neither of the two has allowed himself to melt. But one would need to know Ondine better, I scarcely know her . . .'

The solution of the problem would come to me only if I could sleep with her, thought Fearless. There are women who can be known from outside, with behaviour matching their character. Others can be studied only in intimacy, how they give themselves, what are their pleasure points, what are the defences they make. Ondine was one of the latter. He knew from the Commissar that she had already known other men, at fifteen had been deflowered, had relations regularly since then. At twenty-two she was a woman, in feelings much older than her fiancé, an adolescent of twenty-five.

'I've already told you that a woman must be constantly won,' Fearless said. 'You must not believe that she was won from the moment when she accepted you, that was just the overture. The concert comes later and that is when you see the quality, the artistry of the maestro. Love is an enclosed dialectic of closeness-repulsion, of tenderness and wilfulness. Or it falls into routine, into a cooling of relations and, hence, into mediocrity. I loathe mediocrity! There is nothing worse in man than a lack of imagination. It is the same thing in marriage, it is the same in politics. Life is permanent creation, death and resurrection; routine is the exact opposite of life, it is hibernation. Sometimes, man is like a reptile, needs to hibernate to change his skin. But in that case hibernation is an intense phase of self-dissection, so it is dynamic and creative. Not routine. Avoid routine in love, wretched arguments about everyday problems, go to the heart of things. For you, the essential is the cultural difference between the two of you. You still have not rid yourself of this complex. When you talk about her, there is a latent admiration for her way of speaking, a hunt for her phrases, even her pronunciation. However, you are more broadly cultured than she. Your studies did not go so far, but you have a far higher understanding of life. She knows more physics or chemistry, but is incapable of understanding the profound nature of opposition between the two poles of an electrode and of their essential link. You know little about physics, but are more capable of understanding, because you have known dialectic in life. Your action in the struggle, in which you contribute to transforming society, is a cultural factor much deeper than all the literary knowledge she has. You two could be complementary, as each has much to teach the other. But you shut yourself up in your complex, in the awareness of your lack of culture that is, in the end, only apparent; she feels this and regards herself as intellectually superior, which is only a step from despising you. You are the one who makes her take that step.'

The sun was swallowed up by the foliage. The Commissar dressed. As he put on his boots, he asked:

'What should I do?'

'Win her truly. Win her sexually, as I think you have not done yet. Three months ago, when I saw her, she had all the appearance of someone who was not entirely satisfied sexually. This shows in a woman, believe me.'

'But how to do that?'

'A practical formula? I can't give you that. It's like Marxism. It serves as a guide, an inspiration to action, but does not solve one's practical problems . . .'

He was silent, laughed silently, rubbed the AK. Then he went on:

'I always found it absurd for an individual to get hold of Mao and spend a night reading him, to make a plan for an ambush. Mao offers lessons in strategy, not precise tactics for each moment. The individual must have imagination, study the terrain, and rebuild his tactics. I can give you guidance, but not details of procedure. There are women who like violence, who like to be ravished, others prefer a mental violation, others tenderness, others technique. You must study Ondine, know what is her category and then draw up your plan. In putting the plan into operation, you must be clear, but, at the same time, passionate, intuitive, to be able to change it if necessary. Clearness does not signify coldness in love. You can be spontaneous and clear.'

'Very complicated!'

The Commissar made a gesture of discouragement. Fearless clapped him on the back. At that moment Ekuikui went by, returning empty-handed from hunting. He had the same look of discouragement as the Commissar, with failure putting a hint of shame into his face.

Returning to the Base, where the guerrillas were leaving class to prepare fires and the dinner, Fearless said:

75

'I wanted to avoid it, but it seems that I must go and have a few words with Andre. If food does not come tomorrow . . .'

'You could talk to Ondine. Perhaps you could understand better what the matter is, could advise her . . . and me.'

The voice was a shy entreaty. An effort at detachment, thought Fearless.

'If there's time.'

What a shock it would be for him, if I were to tell him that I could only really know Ondine and advise them properly by studying her sexually. He would never understand, would doubtless lose the total confidence he has in friendship, in my friendship. He is the kind who would hand over his wife to me to take care of . . . I would never do that. Or, if I did, it would already be admitting that anything might happen, and no-one was to blame for what followed. If there is any question of blame! But the Commissar is too young to understand. Anyway, Ondine does not attract me.

They went into the Command hut, where they found several guerrillas discussing the latest issue of the Movement's newspaper that had arrived from Dolisie. The Commissar joined in the discussion, it was his duty.

The Commander stretched out on a camp-bed to smoke. Ondine was not attractive to him? No, that was sure. Not because of being the Commissar's fiancé, he had given up believing in the sanctity of friendship in the context of women. Did Cain not murder Abel because of a woman? He tried to remember the passage in the Bible. Perhaps the Bible does not make it clear. But obviously a woman was at the root of the crime. Ondine must be an artist in bed, it could be sensed, she had fire hidden under the cloak created by her school-girl education in Luanda. It was enough to see how she studied men, appreciated them, weighing their worth, engaging in a duel of looks and being the last to turn away. She had done this with him and with others. She was always prey to knowing if she pleased the man she faced, if a word from her would be enough to arouse him. He had entered the duel, on the first occasion before the Commissar knew her.

She had arrived at Dolisie the day before. He was coming from Kimongo, where he was before the Base. They were introduced by

Kassule, who was now in the East. She faced up to the appreciative glance he threw her, invited him for coffee in her room. She sat on the bed, he remained standing, drinking the coffee. Her short skirt rose and showed her thighs. He looked at them brazenly and let his gaze rise slowly from the knee to the flash of white panties that were hinted at, let it linger, and then continued to raise it to her eyes that shone, challenging, leopard's eyes. She stood up to the look, awaiting the outcome of the examination. He lowered his eyes again, slowly, to her long neck where he saw her throat tighten, on to her small, firm breasts, slender belly, to arrive again at her round thighs. There, Fearless's gaze remained on the key. She waited for his reaction. He did not show discomfiture, of this he was certain.

The conversation had gone on, with him now seated on a bench in front of her. They talked about Luanda, of people he knew and she knew. Ondine sought the duel, did not cease to stare straight at him, with a gleam in the depth of her eyes. Fearless sometimes forgot himself in staring at her thighs, the most exciting thing about her, reminding him of others, except that these were darker. Her look was then discreetly triumphant, but he did not blink or purse his lips or swallow saliva. He maintained the aloof bearing of the Mayombe giant, and the triumph smoothly ebbed from her expression, to be replaced by an ambiguous note of perplexity.

Fearless left and did not allow a further challenge, although she provoked it, even after becoming engaged to the Commissar.

There are women for whom this duel is just a caprice, a futile need to measure one's strength, that goes no further. Not Ondine. Fearless sensed that, in her, what seemed to begin as a game was in the end an imperative need to assess herself and to repair the mask that fell in the duel. What began as a game was in the end a silent invitation. What had made Ondine unattractive to him had been the certainty that she would have been an easy captive for him, too easy, on that afternoon they met. Not that he sought difficult battles only, no. But, when it was a question of a well educated girl, with the studied graces of a city-dweller who was born in the slum and wants to make her way in the centre, then such a person had to be natural and direct, or elusive. Either she played the game or she did not provoke a duel to beg afterwards. Fearless was appreciative of the dignity of a woman who is able to fight for what she wants or who is able to delay the capture, merely to increase the delight of capture. Ondine allowed an equivocal character to show, and that was unattractive to Fearless.

The Commander was at these musings, when VW came into the hut and sat on Fearless's camp-bed. The latter noticed that he had not asked permission, that was a rare familiarity, unknown in VW. The gesture pleased him.

'I'm not a bogey-man any more?'

The lad did not understand the reference. He raised transparent eyes, where fear could be read.

'You sat down without asking permission, as if it were your bed. Which means that you've lost your fear of me . . .'

Other guerrillas were watching the scene from outside the window, but could not hear as Fearless had spoken softly. VW lowered his eyes, waiting for a stronger reaction. If familiarity comes to him because he is my relative, then it is bad; if it is because he is beginning to come out of his shell, if he is beginning to emerge as an adult, then it is good. What was VW's motive?

'Do you think that being my cousin gives you rights the others don't claim?'

'The broadcast is due . . .'

'I know, that's not what I'm asking.' He had raised his voice and those at the window pricked up their ears. 'I am asking you if you think that being the Commander's cousin makes you superior to the rest.'

'No, no, comrade Commander.'

'So, why didn't you ask permission to sit down?'

VW hesitated. He looked behind the Commander, to the group of spectators lined up at the window, without the Commander seeing them. He spoke loudly for all to hear:

'I thought it natural . . . Just as comrade Commander can sit on my bed without asking permission.'

Fearless smiled. VW's shy manner was deceptive; he had character, was now beginning slowly to show his claws. He was not VW, he was a cat, lynx, or leopard. Who knows if not a lion? He would make a good guerrilla. The Commander clapped him on the back.

'You can relax. You have won the right to sit on my bed without asking permission. I doubt if that matters to you, but after all . . .'

VW looked at the window. The murmur that ran through the guerrillas made Fearless realize something was afoot. He stared at VW and saw the triumphant look he was giving his companions outside. Triumphant and reassured. Fearless understood everything: it was not VW's initiative, it was simply a bet he had with the others.

'Go away!' the Commander shouted. 'Get out of my sight, disappear!'

The lad looked at him, puzzled and frightened.

'Get out!' Fearless shouted angrily.

VW put his cap on his head and disappeared. The Commissar spoke from the other side of the hut:

'You have no right to speak to a guerrilla like that, Commander!'

Fearless ground out his cigarette on the floor. He sat on the camp-bed. His eyes glittered as he stared at the Commissar. The latter rose and came to the middle of the hut. Fearless, grim-faced, eyed him.

'I didn't see what happened,' the Commissar said, 'but that is not the way to speak to a guerrilla.'

The Commander stood up in turn. The fighters listened attentively, realizing the tension that had arisen between the two men. The sounds of the forest could be heard, punctuated by the sound of the Commander's foot hammering the ground.

'He is a fraud!' Fearless said. 'You didn't see anything, so don't interfere!'

And he went out of the hut, without looking at anybody. The Commissar was about to speak, but the brusque exit of the other left his words hanging. The guerrillas around the Commissar and the rest at the window were silent, in disappointment that a row between two of their seniors had stopped short.

◆

When Theory came into the group chief Kiluanje's hut, there were present Miracle, Pangu-Akitina, Ekuikui, other guerrillas and, in a corner, whispering to himself private thoughts, the young VW. Theory

79

noticed that Kiluanje stopped his remarks, but, on seeing him, resumed speaking.

'The difficulty here is that the Commander was not in the right and that VW is a guerrilla, before being a cousin.'

'He is his cousin and so has the power to beat him even,' Pangu-Akitina said. 'And it's nothing to do with you.'

'Did you see how annoyed the Commissar was?' Miracle asked. 'If he was in that state, it was because the Commander was in the wrong. The Commissar does not get angry for nothing!'

'Is the Commissar never wrong?' Pangu-Akitina said.

'That's not what I'm saying,' Miracle said. 'But you, because you are Kikongo, just want to defend the Commander.'

'Is that so? And why do you attack him? Because you are Kimbundus . . .'

'Better stop the argument there, comrades,' Theory said.

No-one took any notice of him.

'In Dembos,' Miracle said, 'a fellow like Fearless would not be alive. We'd have wiped him out already!'

'Like they wiped out the assimilated and the Umbundus in 1961,' Pangu-Akitina said. 'But it didn't end there. There'll still be many scores to settle.'

'Comrades, please stop,' Theory shouted, stepping into the middle.

'You think you come here to behave like UPA?' Miracle said. 'Your party is UPA, the party of Kikongos. You come here to sabotage, you are working for imperialism.'

'Leave it, Miracle!' Kiluanje said. 'One day things will be settled, but it's no use now with the tongue.'

'How will they be settled then?' Pangu-Akitina asked. 'How then?'

'It's not important, leave it alone!'

'Comrades, if you go on like this I'm going to call in those in charge,' Theory said.

'You shut up,' Miracle said. 'You have nothing to say, do you hear? We're not talking to you . . .'

'But . . .'

'Comrade Theory,' Kiluanje said, 'you were not asked to come here. So it's better not to interfere.'

'But what you are saying is serious,' Theory said. 'Haven't you understood yet?'

'How not understood?' Ekuikui interrupted. 'They know what they are saying, it is what they feel. Not only the chief and Miracle, but Pangu as well. They know what they are doing and what they want. But as I do not agree, either with one lot or the other, I am going to bed. And let them say, if they want, that it is because I am Umbundu, that it does not affect me, I don't give a damn!'

Ekuikui was on his way out, but Theory held him by the arm. The teacher was trembling and this made Ekuikui stop. The other guerrillas listened with interest, without interfering.

'You can't go, Ekuikui. We must put an end to this argument.'

'Comrade teacher, when there is a tribal argument, it is better to leave it, not to get caught in the middle.'

'A tribal argument?' Kiluanje cut in. 'Who is making a tribal argument here?'

Ekuikui laughed stiffly.

'So I misunderstood, comrade chief. I had understood the talk was about Kimbundus and Kikongos. If that was not said, then there is no tribal argument. I was the one who heard incorrectly!'

'One can talk without it being a tribal argument.'

'How?' Theory said. 'One cannot talk like that. Pangu-Akitina, you'd better come with me.'

'Why must I come, if I'm all right here?'

I'm going,' VW said, 'this discussion doesn't concern me.'

VW went out and no-one held him back.

'You say that things will be settled, but not with the tongue,' Pangu-Akitina said to Kiluanje. 'Settled how? With bullets?'

'Stop this, comrades!' Theory shouted.

'Will be settled, is what I am saying. Do you remember the Tomas Ferreira group murdered by UPA? And all the others? The score is not yet paid . . .'

'And am I from UPA, because I am Kikongo? How am I to blame if UPA does that?'

'The score is not paid, is what I am saying.'

'And the Bailundos who died in '61? Do you think they have

81

forgotten? We were the ones who protected them from you, who came with machetes . . .'

'Comrades, I am going to call the Commissar,' Theory said.

'It's not necessary,' Kiluanje said, 'everything is clear. I won't argue any more either.'

'Stop making your threats,' Pangu-Akitina said. 'Do you think they scare anybody? We have weapons too.'

Theory grabbed Pangu-Akitina's arm and pulled him towards the door. But the medic was stronger and it was Theory who was dragged further into the room.

'You don't scare anybody, are you clear?'

The Kimbundu guerrillas laughed and did not respond. They had held Miracle forcibly, to stop him arguing further. Kiluanje remained calm.

'We have weapons too! They are just over there to threaten . . . Is MPLA yours? The MPLA is not just for the Kimbundus, it is for all.'

The others did not respond. They expected that Pangu-Akitina's shouts, that had already attracted other guerrillas who were peering through the window, would bring the Commissar. Theory tugged him, but the medic repulsed him roughly.

'We wiped out many of you in the past. Dembos and Nambuan-gongo paid tribute to the King of Congo. You were our slaves, how can you talk now?'

The din brought the Operations Chief.

'What's going on here?'

'Comrade Pangu-Akitina came here to insult us,' Kiluanje, the group chief, said.

No,' Theory said. 'They began to argue, I tried to break it up, but on neither side did they want to stop.'

'But who is talking now, and being provocative?' Kiluanje said. 'We shut up, when we saw what Pangu wanted. But he went on and on. Now he's called us slaves of the Kikongos . . .'

'That's a lie!' Pangu-Akitina said.

'It's the truth!' Ekuikui said. 'You were stupid, lost your head, it was what they wanted. Yes, you did say that. But they were the ones who raised the topic and then it heated up. It was not Pangu who came here to insult.'

'All right, the Command will settle this later,' the Operations Chief said. 'Now disperse!'

On their way to the room they shared, Ekuikui said to Theory:

'I don't know if Pangu was tricked or if he wanted to provoke a row.'

'The others were troublemakers. They riled him and then shut up, so that he would drop himself in it. He reacted with tribalism.'

'Obviously, comrade teacher. But it seems to me that he knew this and didn't mind. He was doing it on purpose.'

'To be provocative?'

'Yes, to provoke a tribal clash.'

'But for what purpose?'

'There . . . What men show is never more than a very small part of what they have in their heart.'

'So you think both sides are to blame?'

'Comrade Theory, both want the same thing. When there is a tribal dispute, it is a waste of time to think who is to blame. If on one occasion one provoked it, that is because earlier the other had provoked it. Which came first, the chicken or the egg? Tribalism is like that.'

Theory went into the hut and remained silent. Had his behaviour been the most correct?

What more could I have done? I tried to prevent them, even opposed all of them there, was not afraid to interfere. Was it a sign of progress, of victory over fear? At another time I would have kept quiet or gone away, to avoid difficulties. But I was stronger than myself, did not repress myself, did what came into my head. Perhaps, yes, perhaps it had been a victory.

And he slept, without having a smoke.

I, THE NARRATOR, AM NEW WORLD.

We are seeing something new at the Base now: the Commissar dares to stand up to the Commander.

For progress to be made, it is necessary for an element to form its opposite, which enters into contradiction with the former to negate it.

Fearless, to some extent, created the Commissar by training him. But the fact is that the latter overtakes him in degree of consciousness. Logically, a struggle arises between them, a struggle that is manifest in antagonistic positions in practice. Until now, the Commissar restricted himself to following the Commander, to imitating him: even in gestures, fighting style, the seeming indifference with which he faces the enemy. Today he put himself in public opposition to the Commander, raised his voice to criticize him. Fearless, astonished by his pupil's rebellion, left the Command hut, went walking at night.

The Commander basically is no more than a petty bourgeois dilettante, with anarchist trimmings. Though trained in the Marxist school, he retained from his class origin a good dose of anti-communism, which he shows in his refusal of proletarian equality. It is with poor grace that he accepts the democracy that must prevail between fighters and, sometimes, has sudden acute crises of irrational tyranny. As a verbal defender of the right to revolt, a devotee of permanent contestation, he abuses his position as soon as the contestation is against him. The case of VW exposed all his dictator's mentality. This flagrant abuse of power led the Commissar, who has a more enlightened ideological training, to take a stand in favour of the mass line.

This behaviour leads me to suppose that the balance of power in the Command is going to change. As the Operations Chief says, the Commander's disregard for the opinion of other members of the Command has led to serious mistakes, and the situation was made worse by the fact that the Commissar always agreed with Fearless. But now perhaps we shall see a desirable union between the Commissar and the Operations Chief against the Commander, as defender of petty bourgeois nihilism. There is no need to grieve for divisions between those at the top, they are a historical necessity.

Why did Fearless lose his head? I spoke to VW, knew of the bet they had made, of the words murmured by the Commander. The latter had a superior notion of VW, that he had dared challenge him, and was disillusioned, on discovering that VW's daring was merely the result of a bet. He reacted personally, subjectively, offended because the idea he had formed of VW was false.

It was not VW who disillusioned him, it was he who had illusions about VW.

How can we have confidence in a man with so little objectivity?

The Revolution is made by the mass of the people, the sole entity with leadership capacity, not by individuals such as Fearless.

The future, therefore, will see me in support of proletarian elements against this intellectual who, by virtue of risking his life for subjective reasons, has risen to Commander. War is declared.

Next day, they waited impatiently for midday. Nothing came from outside. Food would only do for that day, then they would have to revert to a diet of roasted 'commons'.

The Commander had woken in silence and his gaze was kept stubbornly on his watch. He did not go out of the Command hut, did not go to train the new recruits. After lunch the hope of seeing a group arrive from Dolisie faded.

'This Andre has cheated me again,' the Commissar said.

'What did you expect?' Fearless replied.

He stood up, picked up the AK, called Struggle and Muatianvua.

'We're going on patrol.'

The three guerrillas left the Base, at a rapid pace, with the Commander at the head. They walked without a break until three o'clock, in the direction of steep mountains that rose always ahead of them. When they reached a stream, Fearless stopped and drank water. The others did the same. Struggle went to observe a path that passed nearby and was mined by them. Muatianvua stretched out to smoke. Fearless was uncommunicative, as he had been since waking that day. Struggle returned to the group, with nothing unusual to report.

'No game in sight even,' Muatianvua said. 'It's almost as if the game is in partnership with Andre to let us die of hunger.'

'If we were united,' Struggle said, 'we would make a coup d'etat, would sack Andre from his position. That's what's needed. But people in the maquis are not united!'

And he looked at the Commander to gauge his reaction. Fearless remained silent. Muatianvua exchanged an understanding glance with Struggle and added:

'If there were a united Command, it could impose certain conditions on Andre . . .'

The Commander lit another cigarette. He contemplated the canopy of the trees in the air, that moved to give an occasional glimpse of blue sky. He pretended not to hear the remarks of his companions and went on smoking, unconcernedly. Mautianvua gave up forcing the conversation and went to look at the river, to see if there were fish. Meanwhile, Struggle looked at the Commander and debated inwardly if he should speak out directly or not. There is something afoot, Fearless thought, it can be felt in the stifling atmosphere at the Base, in the nervousness of the men. And thunder is coming close.

'Let's go to the desert,' he said.

They went on for another half hour and left the forest for a mountain without trees, just grass. They called this desert. Everything is relative. For a man accustomed to seeing leaves up to fifty metres above his head, any terrain on which there is only grass to be found is a desert. In the same way, the savanna would be a Mayombe for the camel. There are still men who demand that their truth be known to everyone, Fearless thought, even if life itself makes us treat everything as relative, even the very vocabulary!

The strong sun of mid-afternoon hurt their eyes and they had to get used to it gradually, with much blinking. They sat at the top of the hill, scanning the horizon. Muatianvua and Fearless stripped off their shirts and left them to dry on the path where they were, a path used by Portuguese soldiers for patrols of the area.

Clouds piled up over the forest, before them. The forest collects clouds, Fearless thought. They come from the deserts and they cross and mingle, over Mayombe. They run freely through space, in essential play of constant distortion – or constant recreation, to be drawn into shapeless mass, to become prisoners of their own component. An isolated cloud has the individuality granted to it by its nervous and capricious changeability; this individuality is lost in the mass that coheres and is valued for its weight, for its savage potential.

Fearless identified with a grey cloud, with white wisps, that scudded in constant revolution, and seemed capable of escape, of passing alongside the mass of clouds that thickened over Mayombe. With beating heart, he followed the frantic movements of the cloudlet that was now a bird, now a light, now the curls of a blonde woman, now a galloping horse. Inside himself he prayed for it to pass to the side of

86

the threatening mass that drew it invincibly. For some moments, it seemed to him that the cloud would pass alongside and would freely follow its precipitate route. But, either through a gust of wind or the attraction, the reality was that the cloudlet was swallowed by the dark-grey mass and broke up in it. A tug at his heart and a gesture of despondency accompanied his voice:

'What's up then, comrades?'

Muatianvua was waiting just for that. He stroked his beard, while his eyes seemed to start from his sharp face.

'What's up is agitation at the Base. Some say that there is no food because the leadership has no confidence in the Base Command, that it is divided. Others that it is because the Commander is no use and does not carry out actions that justify food. Others, just a few, say that it is the fault of the civilians and things must change. There are some for the Commander, the Kikongos; some for the Commissar against the Commander; some for the Operations Chief, against the Commissar and the Commander; some for the Operations Chief and the Commissar against the Commander; in short, these are . . .'

Fearless smiled sadly.

'Are there some for the Commander, without being Kikongos, or for the Commissar, without being Kimbundus?'

'There are, old chap, but not many!'

'As I understand it, some think there are difficulties between me and the Commissar . . .'

'Yes. Since yesterday . . .'

Fearless did not reply. Struggle took advantage of the pause to interject:

'Unity must be made in the Command against the civilians. We have to make a coup against Andre.'

The Commander stared at him fixedly.

'Even with the Operations Chief? You think even with the Operations Chief? You know why I ask, don't you?'

Struggle withstood the penetrating stare.

'Yes, comrade Commander. The Operations Chief can't stand me, suspects me even, but that is natural. The people here don't give support, a Cabinda man is straightaway a traitor . . . But he is a good soldier and will understand one day. I just want the struggle to advance, so I believe it is necessary for the Command to be united and to force the leadership to put someone else in charge in Dolisie. This is the only way the struggle can advance. These people are not treacherous, but need to see that the war is damaging the tuga. The people support what is right, but when what is right shows might. The civilians in Dolisie say that food should not be sent because we are not making war and the Command is divided by tribalism and ambition . . .'

'You harping on about disunity in the Command!' Fearless said. 'Where did they see the Command divided? There are or were difficulties between the Commissar and Ops. I never had difficulties with either of them. The incident yesterday . . . who is trying to blow up yesterday's incident, to make it a bugbear? Yesterday was nothing special. Because the Commissar criticized me? That's very good, he should have done so more often. If they think that this made for difficulties, they are very mistaken, there is no difficulty. None of you give due worth to the Commissar, you think he is soft or a youngster. He has his own head that thinks very well.'

'We know, yes,' Muatianvua said.

'If for once he argues with me, all of a sudden it is because there is something serious behind it! Isn't it natural for two men to argue and even to get angry, especially if they are friends? And I say this to you, who are among the detribalised here, who are not Kikongos or Kimbundus: do not try to turn me against the Commissar, with plots, with so-and-so says, it doesn't work with me. Nor with him.'

'No, we were just reporting what the guerrillas are saying,' Muatianvua said. 'I don't follow one person against another. I follow the one who is right. I don't like plots, I've always spoken man to man. What I said I can repeat in a meeting, with Andre and all.'

'I know,' Fearless said.

Muatianvua was regarded by many as 'anarchist in words'. When he stood up in a meeting, many shook inside: Muatianvu spoke only when he had a bombshell for the discussion, that he threw into the middle of the meeting, with an odd twist to his mouth, hair disordered and eyes darting contempt for the official at fault. He had often been nominated for courses or even promotion. Always there came on the scene someone his words had made an enemy of to sabotage the course or promotion. Muatianvua would shrug his shoulders and say that he had not come for travel abroad – he had this during his voyages as a sailor – or to be a chief; he had come to struggle.

Fearless clapped him on the arm.

'I know. I'm not talking about you, or Struggle. But there are many who were waiting only for a slight argument between the Commissar and me, to start agitating. Many of them don't even know what they are doing. They are mistaken. What unites us, me and the Commissar, is very strong, too strong.'

He was silent, because his voice came with difficulty, with a tightening in his throat. The others respected his silence. Fearless eyed the threatening aspect of the clouds over the path they would take back to Base. He put on his shirt.

'We'll be caught in the rain.'

Not only were they caught in the rain, but no sooner had they plunged into the forest than night surprised them en route. They stumbled on fallen trunks, slipped on the marshy ground, were caught in the creepers that dogged them. Fearless went ahead of the others, impatient to arrive, not for the warmth of his hut, but for the coffee that the Commissar would be preparing, in the knowledge that they would be tired and chilled. And it was not for the coffee, but because it was prepared by the Commissar for him, Fearless.

◆

The Commissar had indeed prepared coffee and filled for him the milk tin that served as a mug. Fearless drank the coffee and lit a cigarette. After smoking, he changed his uniform. Dinner had long grown cold on the plate. The Commissar sat on the bed, beside him.

'I should like to talk to you.'

'About the incident yesterday?'

'Yes.'

'Not worth the bother,' Fearless said.

'Yes, it is worth it. Aren't you going to have dinner now?'

'Later.'

'Let's go outside then. It stopped raining long ago.'

The Commissar was nervous, and his eyes showed him ill at ease.

89

Why discuss? Fearless thought. To dig up what is already dead. Men like to torture themselves with the past and never feel happy unless they are doing so. It is the incapacity to put a stone over an event and advance into the future. There are others, however, who are unable to enjoy life, who see only the future. An incapacity to suffer or enjoy a situation. If they suffer, they console themselves, by thinking that tomorrow will be better. If they are happy, they temper the happiness with the idea that it will soon pass. I live in the present; when I make love, I do not think of the times when I did not enjoy it, or that it will be necessary to wash afterwards. But the Commissar is a child, whose personality wavers between the past and the future. He could perhaps learn to enjoy life, but meanwhile still needs an explanation.

'Let's go,' Fearless said.

They sat on a fallen trunk, at the entrance to the Base, with their weapons on their knees. Muatianvua saw them and did not lift his eyes from the two faces.

'I want to apologize for what happened yesterday,' the Commissar said. 'I should not have spoken to you like that in front of the guerrillas. It undermines your authority and reduces the confidence of the guerrillas in the Command.'

'You were right, I should not have treated VW the way I treated him.'

'But I should not have spoken to you there. I should have spoken to you in private. The guerrillas . . .'

'The guerrillas must become used to hearing those in charge criticized and see that this does not make difficulties among them.'

The Commissar shook his head.

'It was a thoughtless gesture, it was a mistake. Criticism should be made in a Command meeting or in private. That is what one was always told.'

'That is where the damage is,' Fearless said. 'Matters are kept among those at the top. If there is dirty linen to wash, the militant must not know, it is washed in the sanctum. It always remains in the sanctum. How are you going to teach the guerrillas to criticize and be sincere, and to control their seniors, if you do not set examples in practice? I, when I have something to tell you, or Ops, do not call you to the sanctum to criticize, haven't you already noticed? It should be the same with you.'

'You say that! But the guerrillas are already talking, saying there are quarrels among us, that the Command is divided.'

'Precisely because you always dodge making public criticism of me. If you had done that, they would already be accustomed to it and a trivial thing like this would not disturb them.'

'The principle is wrong!' the Commissar said.

'Okay. You need to feel at fault and you are confessing. Until you have made penance, you do not have a quiet mind. Confession you call selfcriticism, contrition you call recognition of error. Do you want me to order you a flagellation to expiate the sacrilege?'

'You see religious thought in everything!'

'Because it is in everything. The Movement cadres are steeped in religiosity, whether Catholic, or Protestant. And not only those in the Movement. Take any Party. There are some who try to cheat the priest and hide their sins: it is like militants who run away from criticism and never accept it. There are others, who go so far as to invent impure thoughts that they do not really have, except at the moment of confession, so that they feel wretched in the face of Christ's suffering: they are the militants always ready for self-criticism, to admit errors they have not made, merely because this gives them the impression of being good militants. A Party is a church. So that is why you think those at the top should criticize themselves on their own, like the priest and the sacristan, who only in the sacristy are accused of stealing their respective lovers, because if they said it in public the believers would become sceptics.'

'It is not the same thing. A Party is not a church.'

'It should not be a church, but it is. Where do leaders argue in public? Nowhere, only within their circle. A militant has to enter the circle, belong to the caste, namely become a leader, to know about the dirty linen that is washed in the highest places. When a leader is criticized publicly, it is because he has fallen into disgrace, is a bishop become heretic, a Luther.'

'So, you think that everything should be done in front of the people?'

'At least of the guerrillas, of militants, vanguard of the people, as one says. You talk so much about the mass of the people and want to hide everything from the people.'

'You, who?'

'You, the political cadres in the Movement. Those who have a solid Marxist training.'

'You have it too.'

'I?' Fearless smiled. 'I am a heretic, I am against religiosity in politics. Am I Marxist? I think so, I know enough Marxism to see that my ideas conform with it. But I do not believe in a range of things that are said or imposed, in the name of Marxism. So I am a heretic, an anarchist, non-Party, a renegade, a petty bourgeois intellectual . . . One thing, for example, that makes me sick is the ease with which you stick a label on a person, merely because he does not have exactly the same view on some or other question.'

'Why are you constantly saying "you", and including me in a group?'

'Because you really form part of a group: the future functionaries of the Party, the higher cadres, who will call for excommunication of heretics such as I. "You" represents all those without a sense of humour, who take themselves seriously and put on serious airs to give themselves importance . . .'

Fearless broke off. The Commissar waited for him to go on. But the Commander seemed to have stopped finally. He lit a cigarette and watched the smoke rings rise in the night and be lost further up in the darkness of Mayombe. Muatianvua went on watching them, from far away. Ekuikui came up to him.

'Are they arguing?'

'Just talking,' Muatianvua said.

'Are they angry?'

'I don't know.'

'If they could agree at least . . .'

'Why should they not?'

The Commissar tapped Fearless's leg. The Commander was smoking, his gaze lost in the night.

'Why did you stop talking?' the Commissar asked. 'So as not to offend me?'

Fearless smiled. He remained silent a few moments more.

'I know that I do not offend you with that. You still have a little understanding, you are not yet totally dogmatic ... This will come, perhaps, but in the meantime you can still hear some home-truths without being offended.'

'At what stage do you think I would be offended?'

'You personally? When the war is over. When you are part of a victorious and glorious Party that has won power and regards as pagan all those who do not belong. When you are in the seat of power, belonging to the narrow group that will control the Party and the State, after the first disillusionment of observing in practice that socialism is not a task for one day and the will of a thousand men.'

'A person does not necessarily become dogmatic ...'

'Then you will have to leave the church!'

'Not necessarily ...'

'Well! We will take power and what will we tell the people? We are going to build socialism. But this will take thirty or fifty years. At the end of five years, the people will begin to say: but such socialism has not solved this and that problem. And it will be true, since it is impossible to solve such problems, in a backward country, within five years. And how will you react? The people are being agitated by counter-revolutionary elements! Which will also be true, since any regime creates its opposition elements, the ringleaders must be arrested, one must pay attention to the manoeuvres of imperialism, the secret police must be strengthened, etc., etc. What is more tragic is that you will be right. Objectively, it will be necessary to tighten vigilance inside the Party, improve discipline, make purges. Objectively it will be so. But these purges will provide pretexts for ambitious men to confuse counter-revolutionaries with those who criticize their ambition and their mistakes. From necessary vigilance within the Party one will pass to a police mentality in the Party and all criticism will be stifled within it. Centralism is strengthened, democracy disappears. What is tragic is that one cannot escape that ...'

'Depends on the men, depends on the men ...'

'On men?' Fearless smiled sadly. 'The men will be prisoners of the structures they have created. Every living organism tends to crystallize, if it is forced to turn in on itself, if the environment is hostile: the skin hardens and gives rise to defensive spines, internal cohesion grows greater and, therefore, internal communication lessens. A social organism, such as a Party, either lives in an exceptional condition that demands constant practical confrontation between men – such as permanent war – or it tends to crystallize. Men who have worked together for a long time have increasingly less need to talk, to communicate, to face each other. Each one knows the other and his views, creating a tacit compromise between them. Contention will, therefore, disappear. Where is contention to come from? The contenders will be confused with counter-revolutionaries, the bureaucracy will be lord and master, and with it conformity, work that is tidy but without passion, incapacity for anything to be questioned and reformulated anew. The living organism, truly living, is one that is able to deny itself in order to be reborn in a different form, or better still, to give rise to another.'

'Depends on the men,' the Commissar said. 'If they are revolutionary individuals and, therefore, able to see what the people's needs are, they could correct all the errors, could change the structures . . .'

'And their age? And the status they have won? Will they want to lose it? Who likes to lose a post? Above all when they reach the age of accommodation, of the comfortable armchair with slippers and the cigars they are in a position to buy? It would be exceptional!'

'There are exceptional men . . .'

'Yes, there are. Once every decade. Can a single exceptional man change everything? Then everything would rest on him and one would fall into the cult of personality, into apotheosis, which comes within the tradition of underdeveloped peoples, religious by tradition. This is the difficulty. In our countries, everything rests on a narrow nucleus, because there is a shortage of cadres, sometimes on one man. How is one to contend within a narrow group? Because it is demagogy to say that the proletariat will take power. Who takes power is a small group of men, on the best of hypotheses representing the proletariat or seeking to represent it. The lie begins with saying that the proletariat has taken power. To belong to the leadership team, it is necessary to have a reasonable political and cultural training. The worker who attains this has spent many years either in the organization or studying. He ceases to be a proletarian, he is an intellectual. But we are all afraid to call things by their names and, especially, this name of intellectual. Are you, Commissar, a peasant? Because your father was a peasant, are you a peasant? You have studied a little, read much, for years engaged in political work, are you a peasant? No, you are an intellectual! To deny it is demagogy, populism.'

'All right. If they should all be intellectuals . . . What has this to do with it?'

'I am not against intellectuals. There are intellectuals who are ashamed of their original sin, who seem to apologize for existing, and shout their anti-intellectualism to the four winds. I am not one of those. What I am against is the principle of saying that a Party controlled by intellectuals is controlled by the proletariat. Because it is not true. This is the first lie, then come the others. It should be said that the Party is controlled by revolutionary intellectuals, who are trying to make policy in favour of the proletariat. But it begins with lying to the people, who see clearly that they control neither the Party nor the State and it is the beginning of mistrust, which is followed by demobilization. I do not say that this is fundamental, mark you.'

'I know. But I think that you are being biased. If one pursues a broadly just policy and succeeds in raising living standards for the people, this will inspire confidence. And that will represent an enormous advance in relation to the current situation . . .'

'Clearly! Commissar, understand me properly. What we are doing is the one thing we must do. Trying to make the country independent, completely independent, is the only possible and humane course of action. For that, socialist structures must be made, I agree. Nationalization of the mines, land reform, nationalization of the banks, of foreign trade, etc., etc. I know that, it is the only solution. And at the end of a certain time, as long as there are not many mistakes nor much embezzlement of funds, the living standard will rise, does not need much to rise. Without doubt that is an advance, and so far we agree, no need for further argument. But let us not call that socialism, because it is not necessarily so. Let us not call it a proletarian State, because it is not. Let us demystify the terms. Let us end the fetishism of labels. Democracy nothing, because there will not be democracy, there will be necessarily, inevitably, dictatorship over the people. This might be necessary, I don't know. I do not see another way, but it is not ideal, that I do know. Let us be honest with ourselves. We are not

95

going to reach 100 per cent, we will stick at 50. Why then tell the people that we are going as far as 100 per cent?'

'How can you say that we shall stick at 50 per cent only? That demobilizes . . .'

'That is what I wanted to show! Like all your group, you think that you cannot tell the truth to the people, or they will be demobilized. Things must be added, things must be exaggerated, to warm the hopes that will make them put up with the early hard times. I, if I were dying, would rather be told, I loathe pious lies. Now, this is what you want to do. So that the dying man should not be disheartened, should not commit suicide, you promise him a cure; the priests promise salvation in the next world. Your Paradise, the Paradise you dangle before the eyes of the masses, is the future as abstract as the Christian Paradise.'

'There is no doubt that you still have metaphysical difficulties. The vocabulary betrays you, Commander!'

Fearless paused. He repeated his automatic gesture of caressing the muzzle of his weapon.

Silence was gathering in the Base, as it drew near to bedtime. But from the Command hut came stifled laughter from guerrillas who were listening to the radio. Muatianvua and Ekuikui, seated at a distance from the two men, were trying to guess from the faces and from the occasional words that reached them whether the mood of trust was restored.

'Possibly,' Fearless said. 'Or it is merely a lingering habit. We all think of death and that is a metaphysical question. But this language expresses my thought well, and so I use it. What I want you to understand, and what it seems to me New World did not see the other day, is that knowing that we shall not reach the promised paradise does not make me fall back.'

'I know, he talked to me about it. He posed this doubt. I answered him that you would not fall back because your reasons for struggle are sincere.'

'What are they?'

'What are they? Well, I don't know! They are humane reasons, belief in the need for justice, hatred of oppression . . . the same as ours. The only difference is in the future. You are more of a man for

96

this phase of struggle, you refuse to think about the future. We think about this future too. How do you see yourself in independent Angola?'

'I? I don't see myself. Simply, and in all honesty, I do not see myself. Is that what shocks you?'

'Well, everyone has his plans ... Where he would most like to work, or rather what his ambitions are.'

'You see yourself clearly, as a political cadre. As for me, I don't see myself. Perhaps in another struggling country ... Who knows, in prison? I do not see myself in independent Angola. Which does not prevent me struggling for that independence.'

'The first time I saw you, no, the second time, you were in a bar drinking beer. People were dancing, the tables were full of chattering couples, as the Congolese bars are. There was a band playing, in an infernal din. I came in with several comrades, there was no empty table. In a corner we spotted you at a table, alone, with a beer bottle before you. You were staring at the empty bottle. Everything seemed to pass you by, the din, the people dancing, the women who went in front of the table, making signs to you. They told me: there's Fearless, section chief Fearless. I was new in the Movement, had recently arrived from Kinshasa, had seen you once in the office. I understood then that you were a lonely man. The rest wanted to speak to you, to sit at the empty table. I managed to persuade them that we go to another bar, to leave you alone. I have never forgotten that scene, you staring at the empty bottle, far away, very far away from the world around you. You are a lonely man, Fearless.'

The Commander nodded in agreement.

'However,' the Commissar went on, 'there is something in you, perhaps the solitariness, that intimidates and at the same time makes people honest with you ...'

'Perhaps the solitariness ...'

'Do you think that's right?'

'We are all of us loners,' Fearless said. 'The hermits of Mayombe! Because we like to live in the forest? Isn't it because we like to feel ourselves alone in the midst of the multitude of trees that surround us? When I was in Europe, I used to like to go in the crowd, at the end of working hours. Anonymous, absolutely anonymous in the midst of the mass. So I like big cities or the forest then, where even if one is not anonymous, rather the reverse, one is noticeable, but where really an individual has a strange sense of personality, as if in the midst of a crowd. So I do not like small towns, which represent the halfway stage of mediocrity. Forgive the chattering, but that is how it is!'

Muatianvua tapped Ekuikui on the leg. He whispered:

'Everything's Okay! It's a friendly chat, mate!'

'Yes, looks as if everything's Okay. Shall we go and rest?'

'No, wait. It's good to keep an eye on them, it's a dark night.'

Theory went out to urinate and found the other two.

'What are you doing here, comrades?'

'Guard,' Muatianvua said, indicating the two faces.

Theory sat down as well, with his gun between his knees, and watched the Commissar and Fearless.

'While the rest want them at each other's throats, you are the only ones watching over them,' Theory said.

'There are more, comrade, there are more!' Ekuikui said.

Fearless lit another cigarette. By the light of the match, the Commissar saw that his eyes were shining. He squeezed his arm.

'Commander, you can have confidence in me. Total confidence! You have a secret, something that makes you a loner, more of a loner than all of us. If you think that it would do you good to tell, you can have confidence. My lips will not breathe a word to anyone.'

'Later, Commissar, later. But don't think it is a terrible secret that makes me a loner. We all have a story, I too have one, but it is nothing special. I was always a loner. When I was a child, I used to hide away to invent extraordinary adventures in which I took part ... as the hero, obviously! It all began with a bashing I took from an older boy, and from which I shamefully ran away. As compensation, I began to make up stories, set in the most varied surroundings, in which the ending was always the same: a duel to the death against this kid. Until I was convinced that making up stories was not enough and that it was necessary to act, to reach this duel to the death. I provoked him and we fought. But I never ceased making up stories in which I was the hero. As I was not the type to remain just making up stories, I had only two courses open in life: to write them or to live

98

them. The Revolution gave me an opportunity to create them in action. If it had not been for revolution, I should certainly have ended up a writer, which is another way of being a solitary. As you see, it is not the terrible secret you think that causes my solitariness, it is a matter of temperament.'

'Know what I think? You should get married.'

'Trop tard.'

'Why?'

'The time has gone. I think that I'm already too used to being my sole master, to be able to share myself. Or I should find a woman I can boss, which is not my style. To live permanently with a woman, respect her wishes, confront her with mine, seek a compromise when the wishes conflict, accept that she, like me, decides on the little and big questions, all this is difficult for me now. I have become too independent. To carry on with an independent life, though married, is not worth the bother. I prefer the independence of life and the dependence of an occasional night. Unless the exceptional woman comes along, the once in a lifetime! Until now I have not met her. But all that takes us a long way from the main subject and because of it I have not had dinner . . .'

'You are right, I am being selfish,' the Commissar said.

'There you go apologizing! If I had not wanted it, I would not have come, or would have cut it short.'

'Do you know what is happening at the Base? There is the Kimbundu camp and the Kikongo. Both camps want a breach between us, so as to have a faction leader, as I understand.'

'Aside from the detribalised elements, who are for our unity,' Fearless said.

'Exactly. Tribal tension has been growing since the mission. The Kimbundus are unhappy because of what happened to Ungrateful and because of Andre . . .'

'About Andre they are right . . .'

'The Kimbundus attribute all the mistakes to Andre, but to you as well. You are the two most conspicuous Kikongos. So they want a row, in such a way that I have to support them against you. The Kikongos, in their turn, defend Andre and want you to put yourself as the Kikongo military leader to expel the Kimbundus from the Command.'

'Bad luck for the Kikongos that I can't stand Andre and don't conceal it.'

'Bad luck for the Kimbumdus that between me and Ops . . .'

The two of them laughed, like two children who are fooling their parents. Muatianvua and his companion heard the laughter and squeezed each other's arms.

'Ops is working under cover,' the Commissar said. 'He was in conference all afternoon with the Kimbundus, even with Theory . . . He called him all alone!'

'Really? Tribalism in him is stronger than racism? I would not have thought it.'

'It is not tribalism. It is ambition!'

Fearless nodded in agreement. The Commissar said:

'He spoke all alone too with New World, who came to sound me out later. What do you think New World is playing at?'

'I think that he would not be involved, once he saw that the basis was tribalism. Perhaps he has not yet realized properly and the theoretical complications confuse him . . . Complications that he sees, but which don't exist, you understand! That lad is really a theoretician, but he has quality, I like him. Certainly he thinks that I am a bourgeois, he is the highest expression of your group of dogmatists. But that will pass!'

'What should we do?' the Commissar asked.

'I think the best thing is to leave things be,' Fearless said. 'If we hold a general meeting, which is what you like because that's what comes in the perfect commissar's handbook, we shall not solve anything, rather give credence to those who think there are hidden quarrels we are trying to camouflage. Let the wave pass, prepare another mission, then meet, in a cooler atmosphere.'

'For once I agree with you about the meeting. But how can we prepare a mission, if there is no food?'

'True. That bastard Andre . . . We have to settle that in the first place. It is not convenient for either of us to leave the Base. Let us send Ops to Dolisie. I know already that he will stay there a week, but there is no other remedy.'

100

'Okay.'

'As soon as he brings food, we shall mount an action. Inactivity causes all kinds of problems. As Miracle says, the war is cold, so law remains cold as well! And we shall only overcome tribalism when the Cabinda people begin to join up. Even the quarrel between Kikongos and Kimbundus will be less acute.'

'We must be very careful not to commit an injustice that could provoke a catastrophe. And to make it clear always that we are unanimous. On the incident with Pangu-Akitina it is better to leave things be.'

'That's it, Commissar. Nothing further?'

'No, the rest can wait for later, you must be hungry.'

'I certainly am. The talk whetted my appetite.'

'For me, it raised morale.'

'Commissar, what does my sudden appetite mean then? Isn't it the same thing?'

They stood up, laughing. They went to the Command hut, as free as the smoke rings that were released in the forest. Reassured, Muatianvua and his companions went to rest.

Soon the palms were sounding the tick of silence.

I, THE NARRATOR, AM MUATIANVUA.

My father was a Bailundo labourer with Diamang, my mother was a Kimbundu from Songo.

My father died from tuberculosis from working in the mines, a year after I was born. I was born in Luanda, the diamond centre. My father dug the virgin soil with a pick, loaded waggons with earth that was to be separated to release the diamonds. He died in the Company hospital, from tuberculosis. My father took with his bare hands diamonds worth thousands of escudos. To us he did not leave one, not even a month's salary. The diamond went into his chest, sucked his strength, sucked until he was dead.

The sparkle of diamonds is the tears of the Company workers. The hardness of diamond is an illusion: it is nothing more than drops of sweat crushed by the tons of earth that cover them.

I was born in the midst of diamonds, without seeing them. Perhaps because I was born in the midst of diamonds, I felt when still young the attraction of drops of sea, those diamond-drops that strike against the hull of ships and leap into the air, with the milky brightness of hidden tears.

I sailed the sea for years, from north to south, to Namibia, where the desert joins the sand on the beach, as far as Gabon and Ghana, and to Senegal, where the green of the beaches turns yellow, until they join up again in Mauritania, linking North Africa to Southern Africa, in the yellow of their beaches. A sailor in the Atlantic, and even in the Indian Ocean, was I. I reached as far as Arabia and again found the yellow beaches of Mocamedes and Benguela, where I grew up. Benguela beaches, Mauritania beaches, Arabia beaches, are they not the yellow beaches of the whole world?

In every port I had a wife, in every port I had a row. Until one day, I was in the Cameroons, I heard on the radio of the attack on the prisons, on 4 February. My ship was returning to the south and I did not reach Angola. I stayed in Matadi, ex-Belgian Congo. Lumumba had died, his wound was still bleeding, the wound was staunched only when 4 February broke out.

Where I was born, there were men of all tongues living in the Company's wretched dormitories. Where I grew up, in Bairro Benfica in Benguela, there were men of all tongues, suffering the same afflictions. The first gang I had belonged to had white kids even, and had kids from fathers who were Umbundu, Tchokwe, Kimbundu, Fiote, Kwanhama.

The women I loved were from all tribes, from Moroccan Riguebat to South African Zulu. All were beautiful and knew how to make love, some better than others, for sure. What is the difference between a woman who hides her face with a veil and one who deforms it with scarification?

Now they want me to be tribalist!

From what tribe? I ask. From what tribe, if I am from all tribes, not only of Angola, but of Africa too? Do I not speak Swahili, did I not learn Hausa like a Nigerian? What is my language, I, who do not say a sentence without using words from different languages? And now, what do I use to talk to the comrades, to be understood by them? Portuguese. To what Angolan tribes does Portuguese belong?

I am the one pushed aside, because I do not follow the blood of my

Kimbundu mother, or the blood of my Umbundu father. Likewise Fearless, likewise Theory, likewise the Commissar, and many more.

The immensity of the sea that nothing can change taught me patience. The sea unites, the sea narrows, the sea joins. We too have an interior sea, which is not the Kuanza, nor Loje, nor Kunene. Our sea, made of diamond-drops, sweat and crushed tears, our sea is the sparkle of a well-oiled weapon that flashes in the midst of the Mayombe greenery, casting diamond scintillations at the Luanda sun.

I, Muatianvua, with a king's name, I chose my route among the world's paths, I, robber, sailor, smuggler, guerrilla, always on the margin of everything (but isn't the beach a margin?), I do not need to support myself on a tribe to feel my strength. My strength comes from the earth that sucked the strength of other men, my strength comes from the effort of hauling cables and turning a crank and exchanging punches at a tavern table somewhere in the world, on the margin of the route of the great liners that pass by indifferently, without ever understanding what makes the diamond-sparkle of the sand on a beach.

CHAPTER 3

Ondine

Food had run out, even the prey hunted by the Operations Chief. The men were going increasingly further away to find 'commons', as the trees that were close to the Base were already exhausted. One had to walk for two hours to reach a virgin spot where there were still fruits. They would go in groups of three and fill their packs. The 'commons' were shared equally among all. There were several guerrillas with diarrhoea, caused by the nut oil. Ekuikui still went out at night and returned at night, in pursuit of game. None could be found. Ekuikui was visibly growing thin, with the thankless effort, but he set out obstinately on the next night.

The Operations Chief had left four days before. He had quickly sent a messenger, to advise that food would soon follow. But the days were passing and the resupply did not come. It might be said that they had not eaten properly for a week. The 'commons' were nutritious, but did not kill hunger, as they were used to manioc, that fills the stomach without nourishing. The feeling of hunger increased the isolation.

The Commissar ran hither and thither, settling the disputes that multiplied. Several guerrillas threatened to desert even, but this remained words. Fearless had told the Commissar to avoid awarding punishment in cases of tribal quarrels, as hunger accentuated nervousness and tribalism. The Commissar did not want to accede, but in the end he realized that the situation was abnormal and that irritation spread to everyone. He became a mediator between adversaries, instead of a judge.

New World had noted the change in the Commissar's attitude. One day he asked to speak to him. They were by the river and the Commissar agreed.

'Comrade Commissar, it seems to me that you are being very liberalistic. There have been serious matters, very serious indeed, here at Base, and the Command has made no comment on them. It is

104

obvious that the only thing missing is shots! Comrade, instead of ensuring discipline, you are trying appeasement.'

'People are hungry, comrade. Brains don't work well with hunger, still less nerves. We cannot act with the same strictness as at a normal time.'

The Commissar's eyes were fixed firmly on the river, as if he expected to see a shoal of fish. He had already thought of going as far as the Lombe to fish, but it would not repay the effort and risk, and besides, there was no salt.

'I think one cannot compromise. The situation gets worse still. Everyone will take advantage of the excuse of nerviness to let go. I think that you comrade, as Commissar, should be unbending.'

'No, that would just provoke a total rebellion, that could not be justified afterwards.'

'One can't shrug off discipline just for fear of a rebellion.'

'Depends on the occasion, on the circumstances.'

'No, comrade Commissar, I cannot agree. That is a compromise, opportunism even. There are strict questions, such as discipline . . .'

'Discipline is not the difficulty. It is punishment for indiscipline. When the situation changes, there will be criticism of those who are now behaving wrongly. But not now. Everything depends on circumstances.'

'There are some things that are above circumstances. You can't go into a hut without finding an argument. Because my ration is smaller than yours, because the supervisor gave you an extra ration, etc., etc. That's no good. If anything serious occurs, the responsibility will be yours.'

'I have never run away from responsibility, comrade New World, you do not have to remind me of that. And I am ready to defend my view on any occasion.'

'That will be too late, for the damage will already have been done. Disciplinary matters are within your domain, so you must decide them with complete authority and without seeking anyone else's view.'

'Thank you for the advice, but I know my work. And I ask the opinion of whom I please . . . I'm even obliged to listen to the views that are forced on me, such as yours . . .'

105

The Commissar turned his back and went off to Base. New World clenched his fists to avoid shouting out. 'Teleguided,' he muttered between his teeth. 'The Commander caught you without Ops, turned you in the opposite direction and put you in his pocket.'

The Commissar went straight to the Command hut. Theory and Fearless were there. The Commissar threw himself on a camp-bed, trying to simmer down.

'Have you heard the announcement given on the radio just now?' Fearless asked. 'Some guerrilla was captured and made statements. Statements against us, certainly! It might be a lie, but might also be true.'

'I didn't hear,' said the Commissar.

'They say it was in Moxico.'

'It traps a bloke to be a prisoner!' Theory said. 'He remains isolated, against everyone. Every face he sees is an enemy and there you are alone, in the middle of them. It's hard, there's no doubt it's hard. What can you do in such a situation? There are some who resist, others talk. I have the impression they talk more because of the isolation, than because of any actual physical suffering.'

'It depends on individuals,' Fearless said. 'Both factors count, in some individuals one factor more than the other.'

'And later, in prison . . . with the interrogation already finished, years inside, face to face with oneself. It would drive one mad! I understand that blokes can't stand up to it . . .'

'I seems to me there are three types of individual faced with prison,' Fearless said. 'In the first place there are the ones who conform; they are the angry ones, who let themselves be destroyed, who complain constantly but who deep down accept the shame. That is why they complain. Formally, apparently, they are the most unconformable, because they yell, protest, cry. But that in the end is a form of acceptance. Noncomformity lies in rational and coherent behaviour. These are merely characterless types, for whom tears and shouts are no more than an external means of believing themselves still in revolt.'

'Great!' Theory said. 'Go on.'

The Commander looked at the Commissar, who was trying to keep his eyes shut. A frown appeared on Fearless's forehead.

'Then there are the nonconformists, who struggle to escape, who

106

prepare plans and make new ones as soon as the former fail, who live in direct opposition with the guards, who are always being beaten but get up again afterwards.'

'And then?'

'The third type comprises the calm nonconformists. Seeing that escape is impossible, they organize themselves, they stir up the other prisoners, they find a way of studying, writing, etc. They never moan, because they know it is useless. They do not attempt individual escape, because it is useless. And they loathe useless gestures, that merely dissipate the capacity for revolt.'

'I see you in the second group,' Theory said.

'I should prefer to see myself in the third group,' Fearless said. 'But perhaps you're right. One does not always succeed in being what one wishes.'

The guerrillas outside were calling Theory. It was time for classes. Classes were followed with scant attention. But the Command and the teacher insisted on them, because, in any case, they helped pass time and forget hunger. Theory suffered, in a weakened condition and having constantly to speak, but he put up with his duty.

The Commissar and Fearless remained alone. Fearless switched off the radio.

'What's up, Commissar?'

'Why do you ask?'

'You have the expression of someone who's bumped into a bear!'

'I did have a bump! That New World . . . caught me by the river, gave me an earful because I was letting discipline at the Base go to pot. That I should be harder, that I was taking liberalist attitudes . . .'

'That's good coming from him!'

'That I should be responsible if one day there was shooting, that I should take no notice of other people's views. By that he meant that I should take no notice of your view. But he was shouting out his views to me. Just imagine!'

'And you?'

'In the end I turned my back. Sure the situation is delicate, one doesn't really know what to do. Everyone is on edge and this must be taken into account, but equally one must not let things rot.'

107

'So what do you think should be done? Clap irons on two guerrillas who quarrel?'

'No, not that.'

'Put them on extra guard?'

'With this hunger, no-one would stand more than the usual guard duty. They will fall asleep on guard.'

'So?' Fearless asked.

'Don't know, don't know. But I also think that one cannot neglect . . .'

'Obviously, I think so too. The difficulty is that one can't give punishment now. But you must criticize the wrong-doers, very severely even, not merely record.'

'That's just what I do!'

'So, what do you want to change in your approach?'

'I, nothing. New World is the one who wanted.'

'It seemed to me just now that you were not totally sure of your ground.'

The Commissar eyed Fearless, and rose on the bed to a sitting position.

'Can anyone be sure in this situation? Tell me, Commander, can anyone be sure?'

'Yes, they can. New World! He has a Bible . . . The whole truth is written, graven on stone, not even two thousand years of history can change it. Blessed are the believers in the absolute: for they shall have peace of mind! Don't you want to be blessed, most sure of yourself? Find a catechism . . .'

The Commissar smiled. He lay down again.

'What should we do?'

'Nothing. Wait.'

'The people are so far away!' the Commissar said. 'If there were people close by, they could have given us food. That village where we were on the last mission could supply us. We have to take the Base further inside, over in that area. It could supply us, don't you think?'

'Could, could have . . . Now it only remains to wait for Ops. If mister Andre deigned to open his purse.'

'But maybe he hasn't any money?'

'Who?'

'Andre.'

'He must have money, yes. That is sabotage.'

'But why?' the Commissar asked.

'Go there and see why a bureaucrat sabotages the war! Maybe because the war leads to the training of more cadres, who may one day replace him ... Maybe because things must be done within rules that he made for himself and that he cannot adapt in any way. Who knows! I don't understand either. Since he does not keep the money for himself, but squanders it on women. He squanders enough on them, and has a string of lovers they say. But he should take the money from other less fundamental sections, the civilian sections, so that the war should not suffer from his night life. That is what any dishonest but intelligent type would do. Not he. He goes and sabotages just the section that could eliminate him. Since it would be easy for us now to provoke a rising. What could be easier than taking the guerrillas to Dolisie to arrest him? Child's play! That would force the leadership to take steps, and whatever they were, he would have to stir his stumps elsewhere. I often wonder if that is not the only answer left us ...'

'Why do you not put it into practice?'

'Which guerrillas would not do it? Only the Kikongos. But even they would march perhaps, if I persuaded them.'

'I don't know. Andre always slips them money, when they go to Dolisie.'

'That's the heart of it! Not to all. Pangu-Akitina himself complains. And even if the Kikongos were unwilling, they are a minority who would not stand in the way, if I was with the rebels.'

'You would lose all prestige with them.'

'If you knew how fed up I am with this tribal prestige! If I don't do it, that's not why.'

'Why then?'

'Perhaps because it is too strong an act of rebellion, perhaps overdoing it in relation to the seriousness of the case. Or perhaps because I have a secret hope of another answer ...'

'That one now!' the Commissar said. 'If there were another, I shouldn't wonder. But I am astonished to hear you talking like this.'

'What do you want? Perhaps I am less anarchist than you think . . . And you, would you be the man to lead this rising?'

'I have already thought about this as well. I would be capable, if it arose from a meeting of militants. If the majority of militants demanded it. Why not? What is at issue is the struggle. Our latest action showed that there are conditions for the struggle to spread here. What is missing is organization. Therefore Andre is sabotaging the development of the war. It is the militants' right to clean him out. But it would have to be a decision taken by the great majority of militants.'

'You are being demagogic! You know that a majority would march if we two took a position in favour of this rising. So do not say that you would submit to the view of the mass, when you know perfectly well that you can influence that mass.'

The Commissar was about to reply, but Struggle abruptly entered the Command hut.

'Comrade Commander, may I go hunting?'

'So late?'

'I was at the river and I saw a blue bird in the sky. It is a lucky sign. There is game near here. For sure I shall find something, that's what the bird meant.'

'You and your superstition!' Fearless said. 'Go, go away with you. You'll be saying that I am to blame for hunger at the Base, because I do not let hunters marked by Providence go hunting. Obviously if you don't find anything, you will still believe in birds.'

Struggle shrugged his shoulders. He went out.

'When will you put an end to such beliefs, Commissar?'

'Not even after twenty years of socialism!'

The Commander switched the radio on again. The government station was playing dance music.

'We were talking about a rising,' the Commissar said. 'I must tell you that if I never spoke to you of that, it was for fear of encouraging you. I thought you would soon seize on the political imprimatur,' (the Commissar stressed the term), 'to make a speech to the guerrillas and give the order to attack, as if it were an operation . . .'

'As you see, you were thoroughly mistaken.'

110

Fearless is indecipherable, the Commissar thought. Really the lines are never straight.

'Do you know something, Commander? I feel like smoking.'

'This villain! You never smoke . . .'

'Sometimes I have an urge.'

'Take a cigarette. Don't choke!'

Fearless held out the packet. The Commissar took a cigarette, then put it back in the packet.

'No, doesn't matter. The cigarettes are almost gone. I don't have the habit, it is selfish to smoke one of the few you have left.'

'You are right, I don't insist. I've three left. Hunger I put up with easily. But a shortage of tobacco is worse. And the less one eats, the more one needs to smoke. What shall we do if Ops does not come today? We will definitely have to march on Dolisie.'

'Just because of your cigarettes?'

'Certainly! There I should have a serious motive that would make me forget my scruples.'

The Commissar laughed. A young laugh in which all his muscles shared the effort. Fearless, no. Fearless's laughter seemed to come from much deeper and came out in a roaring burst. The Commissar's laugh came from the skin, his own came from the belly, Fearless thought. Was it age that led laughter to bury itself in the body? How will I laugh in ten years' time? A low giggle, without moving the lips, hoarse sounds escaping an old throat. Hoarse, like the lion, perhaps. That's it, the lion is always associated with the idea of old age. And twenty years' time? At fifty five? Well by then I will not be alive, for sure. The laugh will come from a grave, a metre below ground, perhaps deeper, and will shake the memorial stone with the name and dates. If there is a memorial . . .

Fearless went to train the new recruits. The Commissar went to sit in on the classes, to pass the time and to encourage the teacher and his students. The recruits were complaining of weakness, they were not used to such a diet. Fearless made himself deaf to their complaints, he made them carry out the usual exercises, although he allowed more rest periods and did not insist on the more difficult ones. VW continued to avoid contact with him, so the Commander always placed him near to himself and chose him as partner in the exercises in pairs. VW obeyed, but did not open his mouth. Is he offended or ashamed? Surely both.

School and training were interrupted by a warning from the guard: a group of men was approaching. The guerrillas abandoned what they were doing, ran to the entrance to the road, forgetting their weapons even. They knew it could only be the Operations Chief's resupply group. The hugs between those who were arriving and those who were waiting showed not only the joy of meeting but also appreciation for the breach in the isolation. The atmosphere spread immediately through the Base, with a mixture of shouts and laughter and hugs.

But the Operations Chief did not bring only the resupply. He called the Commander aside:

'I've brought an item of news. Comrade Commander is the most suitable person to deal with the case.'

'What's it about?'

'There's a row in Dolisie. That's why we took so long. It was impossible to locate Andre, who is still in hiding from the militants. His assistant was the only one I could contact. In the end he found this food, but it took a long time.'

'So what's happening?'

'Something serious, there's a lot of confusion ... Comrade Andre and comrade Ondine were caught ... They were caught in the bush! It's like a powder keg, Dolisie is almost on fire. I don't know what to do about the Commissar. Everyone knows, he should know.'

Fearless leaned against a tree. He lit a cigarette. The Operations Chief noticed that the Commander's hand was shaking.

'What should I do, comrade Commander?'

'You do nothing, you say nothing.'

'And will he remain like that?'

'No, I shall speak to him,' Fearless sighed. 'Who should speak to him, if not I?'

'But I'm bringing a letter from Ondine for him.'

'Really? Deliver it. Then I will speak to him. Are you sure it is true?'

'It's true, comrade Commander. To the extent that a comrade from the leadership was expected today to settle the matter.'

They returned to the Command hut. The Commissar was there

with several militants. The Commissar was lively, while the rest were reserved and speaking ceremoniously. The Commissar was not noticing, but Fearless understood at once. The Operations Chief looked at the Commander. The latter with a nod told him what to do.

'There's a letter here for you, comrade Commissar.'

The Commissar recognized the writing. A smile crossed his lips and, especially, his eyes. He broke off the conversation, tore open the envelope and sat down on the bed. Fearless observed his reactions. And he saw the Commissar pass slowly, in the slowness with which he read the letter, from a state of delight to stupefaction, then to disbelief, to end in apathy. He stretched out on the bed, staring at the thatch in the roof, with the letter in his hand. Ondine had explained everything, evidently.

What could be done? The best thing was to leave him to come out of the apathy of his own accord. When he had passed into despair, then certainly would be the moment to intervene.

The Commander went to the kitchen to order a huge lunch to be prepared, but the duty man had already taken the initiative. Groups were whispering. The news passed from the mouths of those who were arriving from Dolisie to the ears of those who were at the Base. For once at least, Fearless thought, the one most concerned was not the last to know. One would need to know the details of the matter before forming an opinion, but for the first time he felt a certain admiration for Ondine, as she had been willing to take the first available opportunity to report what had happened. That at least was a mark in her favour . . .

The Operations Chief came up.

'There are going to be big problems in Dolisie, comrade Commander. As I told you, the leadership has already been informed. It will be necessary to replace comrade Andre.'

'Not before time,' Fearless said.

'It seems to me that comrade Commander should go there. And the Commissar as well.'

'The Commissar may go if he wishes. That is a personal matter, we do not have to interfere. I'm thinking too that I should go there, that is an organizational matter. But where is Andre?'

'In hiding. He's afraid of the militants' reaction, so they say. Since

113

the tribal matter will come in as well. They were watching the trains and he didn't take any of them. He must be in Dolisie, unless he hitched a lift by car to Brazza.'

Andre was Kikongo and Ondine engaged to a Kimbundu. One did not need to be a magician to guess the atmosphere that would prevail in Dolisie, Fearless thought. Andre had finally buried himself. So long as he had Congolese lovers, people murmured but did not care to act. Now it was different. What was tragic was that the inevitable had come to Andre, at the expense of the Commissar, which was unfair. How should we know what is fair and unfair, when there are women involved!

Was it not because of a woman that Cain murdered Abel? If it does not say so, the Bible has shamelessly hidden the truth.

◆

Returning to the Command hut, Fearless found the Commissar preparing a pack. The latter stared at him. Fearless noted the glazed look and was disturbed. Useless to try to hide things or beat about the bush, it was the moment to act.

'Where are you going? To Dolisie?'

The Commissar did not respond. He rolled his blanket, put it in the pack and tightened the straps. The Commander put a hand on his shoulder.

'You don't want to talk a little?'

The other did not respond. He put the pack on his back, picked up his weapon and canteen.

'Commissar, answer, where are you going'

The Commissar turned towards him, moved his lips and, suddenly, turned his back and went out. Fearless grabbed his AK and went after him.

The Commissar was moving quickly. He went past the sentry, crossed the river, took the short-cut to Dolisie. The Commander followed at a distance of ten metres. They marched for fifteen minutes, fording the rivers. The Commissar seemed unaware of the presence of Fearless. He is going along blind and deaf, the latter thought. It is dangerous to move thus in the bush.

114

Meanwhile, the Commissar stopped and looked behind him.

'What do you want, Fearless?'

'I'm going with you.'

'Why?'

'You did not tell me where you were going. I am the Commander, I have the right and duty to follow anyone who leaves the base illegally. Or even to arrest him, if I deem necessary.'

'I am not going to run away.'

'Who will guarantee me that?'

'I am not a deserter.'

'You are in a situation as deserter, since you did not report where you were going.'

'You know very well where I am going.'

'I do not know, because I was not informed. You may think it bureaucracy, but it is my duty.'

'Anyway,' the Commissar said, 'I'm being fooled around. Let them treat me as a deserter, if they wish. If you think I have much respect for your organization . . .'

'You cannot condemn the organization for the reprehensible behaviour of one man in charge.'

'They are all the same. They always take advantage of being in charge to . . .'

'You too are in charge, Commissar!'

The Commissar shrugged his shoulders. They were face to face now on the path, the Commissar holding his weapon in both hands, the Commander with his weapon on his shoulder.

'Let's sit down and discuss,' Fearless said.

'There's nothing to discuss!'

'You're an idiot! You're going to Dolisie to do what? I'm going to Dolisie too. I was thinking of going tomorrow, it is very late already today and we must take the chance to eat. If you like, you can come with me. Moreover, it is better that the two of us go, as there will be serious political matters to settle.'

'I am fed up with political matters!'

'All right, I know. I understand perfectly how you feel, believe me. But why desert if you can go legally? Why lose part of your justification in the Movement's eyes, merely for a thoughtless gesture?'

'It is not desertion, because you are already informed. Anyway, I am a member of the Command and can take my decisions. I'm not concerned about the Movement.'

'Don't force me to be a defender on behalf of the Movement against you, Commissar. I, the anarchist, preventing the Political Commissar showing disrespect for the Movement . . .'

'What does the Movement give militants? Just knives in the back.'

'Don't confuse one irresponsible official with the organization.'

'They are all the same!'

'They are not and you know it.'

Fearless held out to him the packet of cigarettes that had come with Ops. The Commissar accepted. They both smoked.

'Let's sit down. Smoking on foot is no pleasure.'

The Commissar obeyed. First round won, Fearless thought. Now it is a question of acting with great care.

'What would you do if I went on walking?' the Commissar asked.

'One of two things: either arrest you or accompany you. I am undecided. The first repels me, nor is it fair. The second hypothesis pleases me much more, but I did not inform the Base, nor bring a pack.'

'You would never arrest me.'

'I would be obliged, since I cannot let you go alone. You would be caught on the road at night.'

'You would never arrest me!'

'You think not?'

The Commissar threw away the cigarette.

'What are you going to do at Dolisie, Joao?'

For the first time, Fearless had addressed him by name. The name Ondine used.

'Settle this matter.'

'In what way?'

'Don't know!'

'Isn't it better to think a little, and for us both to go tomorrow?'

'I must see her, talk to her . . . I can't decide anything without talking to her.'

'Agreed! But it's better tomorrow. You will arrive at night, without

116

a pass. Obviously this is not serious, but . . . If they want, they can make difficulties for you.'

'Do you imagine that anyone will ask me for a pass? They will all run away from me, as if I had scabies that must be avoided, since no-one can talk to a scab . . . I can desert, I can insult, anything is allowed me, since I have scabies. A scabies that is incurable, a scabies that lasts till death, like shame. Cuckold! I am a cuckold, do you understand? And do you come to talk to me about trifling formalities, such as a pass . . . I know that you are looking for some excuse, want to keep me at the Base, are afraid that I should go like this at night. Okay! Why are you using such tricks?'

Fearless turned his gaze to the path. One day, the Portuguese would discover this path that was over-used and they would go straight to the Base. The colonialist trackers were already searching for it, news that the Base was inside had already reached their ears, through spies infiltrated in the Congo. Perhaps at that very moment they were in an ambush. One could not be too careful. And the Commissar had run along this path, without a care for the light breaking of sticks that a prudent foot makes.

'You can't talk like that, you don't know for certain what happened.'

'Ondine wrote to me. She told me everything.'

'Was it a steady relationship or was it by chance?'

'By chance, once. By chance no, that never happens by chance. If she still liked him, I would understand. I had a foreboding even one day, but it was something very vague. But she says that she does not like him, that it happened . . . I don't understand, Commander, don't understand. I make the effort but don't succeed in understanding.'

I understand, Fearless thought. But who can say finally that he understands, that he is sure of something?

'It seemed that she liked me, although with some difficulties, even in the letter she let that be understood . . . But I don't know. Says that she is going away, asking for a transfer, asks forgiveness . . . I'm unable to understand, Commander. Why, why, oh why?'

Fearless let him weep. It was just what Fearless wanted, that he should weep. Like a child. And he played a mother's role and let him weep on his neck. He put an arm round his shoulders. He felt in his own body the convulsions in the Commissar's body and recalled another moment when he had felt in his own body the convulsions of the stabbed traitor. The same sensation came over him and he wanted to push the Commissar away. Panic took possession of Fearless, embracing a dying Commissar who shook. He could not push him away, he must cradle him on his neck and allow all the anger, all the despair that had built up in him, to escape. Fearless stoically bore with the disagreeable sensation, until the Commissar was calmed.

The latter stood up, picked up his weapon and trekked back, in the direction of Base. Fearless followed him. When they reached the first river, the Commissar stopped and put his head in the water. He withdrew his head from the water to breathe and then ducked it again, until he was breathless. He repeated the operation five times. At the end, he sat on a rock. Water ran from his head and dripped down his neck, soaking his shirt. He rose with a start.

'I am going to Dolisie.'

'Rubbish! Wait and we'll go tomorrow.'

'I must see her today. I must be at rest.'

'At rest how?'

'Know what really happened.'

'And Andre? What are you thinking of doing about him?'

The Commissar eyed Fearless. A pure gaze, childlike, darkened by tears. This is how you are becoming a man, Fearless thought. Becoming a man is to make a shell about one, full of projecting spines, an increasingly hard shell, impenetrable. It hardens with the blows one suffers.

'Nothing. Obviously I'm not going to do anything to him. The Movement will take care of it.'

'I thought you wanted vengeance.'

'Vengeance for what? He didn't rape her!'

'But a while ago you were saying that all those in charge are the same, that they abuse their power.'

'That's a matter for the organization. His failing is in regard to the Movement, he is an official who failed in organizational discipline. I have nothing to do with that. My concern is with her.'

'You mean you have confidence in the Movement, then . . .'

'How could I not, Commander? What would I be without the

Movement? An orphan. If the Movement still has types like you, then how could I not have confidence?'

'Careful! These ideas are dangerous and mistaken. Then you fall into the cult of personality . . .'

'What an idiot I am! There you are pushing the argument, to distract me and delay me, and I am falling into the trap . . . I'm going at once. Let me pass!'

'No, Joao, you shall not pass. We'll go tomorrow.'

'Let me pass!'

The Commander was on the path to Dolisie, with his weapon on his shoulder. The Commissar aimed an AK at him.

'I am going to pass, Fearless. Don't try to stop me.'

'Don't do that, Joao, or I shall have to arrest you.'

'Try, if you can.'

The Commissar advanced, with the weapon aimed. Fearless studied his eyes. He went forward a step. A brilliance shone in the Commissar's gaze. A sudden brilliance that swiftly vanished. Fearless went forward another step. The muzzle was touching his belly. Fearless pushed away the muzzle with his left arm, keeping constant watch on the Commissar's eyes. He took hold of the muzzle and pulled it. The Commissar let go of the weapon. The Commander calmly slung both weapons on the same shoulder.

'Let's go to the Base. Forward!'

The Commissar went unprotestingly in front.

Near the Base, Fearless handed him back his weapon.

'This is between us.'

When they entered the Base, it was two o'clock and lunch was ready. The Commissar went to the Command hut. Fearless asked the guerrillas not to disturb him. And he went to the kitchen to fetch food for them both. The Commissar refused the plate. Fearless did not insist, he left the plate on the table. In the end the Commissar took his, eyed it with a shamefaced smile and began to eat.

'Excuse me, give me another cigarette.'

The Commander held out the packet.

'Don't tell me you're taking up smoking now.'

'I could. Don't they say that a cigarette is the only faithful

119

companion?' Fearless felt the other's bitterness. He lit a cigarette for him without retorting. Then he lit his own.

◆

'The other day you wanted to know my secret, do you remember? Still want to hear it?'

'Yes.'

'I think the moment has come. So let's go to the river. It is our confessional.'

They went. They sat on a trunk. Fearless took off his boots and put his feet in the water.

'You should do likewise. It's one of the most pleasant sensations.'

'Perhaps,' the Commissar said. 'But, if the tuga appear, you leave your boots and have to run away barefoot, which is not at all pleasant.'

'It happened to me once.'

'I know.'

'As you see, there are mistakes that are not corrected. But you wanted to know my story. All right then! In Luanda I lived with a girl, I was twenty-four. She was named Leli, she was of mixed blood. In 1960 we began to live together. We did not get married because of complications with her family. Her father was a businessman and wanted his daughter to marry a white. To improve the breed! But things sorted themselves out. By ill luck, Leli convinced herself that she fancied someone else. One day she came to me in the house saying that she was leaving. I was already apprehensive of something, as lately she had been absent, cold, always irritable. I was a kid, without much experience. She was my first real woman, previously I had known only prostitutes. A string of them, to tell the truth, but that was not enough. The tactics are completely different, with a prostitute there is practically no balance of strength to be established, everything is on the basis of money. Unless you are the pimp, then it is all right. But I was never a pimp, knew almost nothing about the whole skill of controlling someone else.'

'They say there is a great art in being a pimp,' the Commissar said.

The Commander did not catch what he said. He went on with his memories:

120

'It was a terrible scene, her crying in one corner, and I in the other. No, she had never slept with him, but it was what she wanted most in life. In the end she stayed with me a while longer. And I learned no lesson! It seemed that things had quietened down, but the truth was they were merely postponed. I was doing secret work, had sometimes to go to Caxito or Dalatando. My job suffered for it, but that didn't bother me. She was bothered, said that I was looking for women, that I did not want a good social position, that she was the one to suffer the misery, etc. I regarded this as jealousy and took it calmly. If she was jealous it was because she loved me. How innocent! Jealousy and love are independent, at least in this society. All right then. One day she came and repeated that she was going to see the other man. And she left the house. That night I wrestled with the most acute jealousy. I wanted to run through the neighbourhood in search of her, I imagined killing them both, heaven knows what! Then I understood that our life was very dull, the transports of love had ended in the first year, and Leli was insatiable. I decided that I must win her back. She came back, ahashed, the next morning. She told me that she had not had the courage to go and see the other man, had slept at a girl-friend's house. I understood that she was sufficiently taken with me, but needed to have a bad experience elsewhere, to be ready to be won back.'

'So you pushed her . . .'

'Exactly. I told her that I wanted nothing more to do with her, was going to find another woman. That released her from me, but, at the same time, shocked her. The fact of losing me made her hesitate immediately. I controlled the desire to tell her the truth and explained that during the night I had reflected and that, after all, she no longer attracted me. Leli did not know what to do. I saw her forsaken. At that moment I felt that I had conquered her, it was just a question of time.'

'Why didn't you recover her there and then?'

'It was necessary to consolidate the victory. She went to live with the other man. He was a postal worker, with intellectual aspirations, very conceited. And basically, empty. I used to meet Leli often, behaved to her like a best friend, a confidant. In front of her I put on the air of a libertine, accepting everything. For the first month, Leli

121

did not belong to me, she belonged to the other man. But I observed disillusionment grow in her, as time passed and she knew the other man better. Unwittingly she had to compare him with me, the new man, now adult, who had risen before her. With great subtlety I shaped the personality I must show her. And she began to regret her choice. I appeared frequently with girls and sensed her jealousy revive. Leli was always a good actress, but I knew her too well to be fooled: Leli was jealous of any girl I showed an interest in. It was still too soon to act. I allowed her to become totally disillusioned with the other man. We dined together practically every day and she confided in me her miseries. Surreptitiously, I encouraged her to see the other man's conceit, his pretentiousness, his backward ideas. The petty bourgeois type. Leli was not petty bourgeois, she had more the failings of a grand bourgeois than of a petty bourgeois.'

'Heavens! You must have been cool . . . Even made a class analysis?'

'No, I'm only explaining that now, I couldn't have done it at the time.'

Fearless took his feet from the water and rubbed them absent-mindedly.

'From the second month, it was already clear that Leli was fed up with him. Just sexually there was still a certain tie between them. It was in this field that I had to act. There came a night when she confided in me that she was going to find a lover. She had never done that to me, because she respected me. But him . . . She said it in a casual way, more as if to find out my view. That night I invited her to my house. I put on records, we danced and, in the end, I struck. She realized what had happened only after we had already made love. She still tried to remonstrate with herself, but I told her that it was the most natural thing, that she had nothing for which to blame herself. We made love all night long. Next day, she went to fetch her things from the other man's house.'

The Commander fell silent, his eyes lost in vacancy.

'And then?'

'We lived like that for two months. Now comes the difficult part to tell. While we were separated, I became used to the new personality I had constructed. All the effort to overcome jealousy, to think of her as a victim to be brought down, had made me hard. I ceased to care

122

for her or, at least, to care for her completely as I had before. I needed to break free from her, from the influence that Leli had over me. For that I had to win her back, to feel superior to her, to be able to act rationally, driven by reason alone, without feelings. After winning her back, I felt freed.'

'You were revenged, isn't that it?'

'If you like, my self-esteem was restored. I began really to discover all the mischievous side of Leli that until then I had not discovered. The habit of having other women led me in search of other women. I was no longer faithful to her. She knew it, but forgave me. She thought I was doing it for belated vengeance. She was shocked at what had happened and was still amazed that I had accepted her. I don't know if you understand, but the difficulty is that she realized she loved me irresistibly when she felt that she had lost me. After that, she was trying to hide the realization from herself.'

'And so?'

'At the end of two months, I analysed myself deeply. At a table in a bar, as I always do when I want to be honest with myself. I analysed myself and saw that I was freed. Nothing remained. The past was dead, I was not even moved at thinking of the other man or of Leli in the arms of the other man. So I decided to put an end to it. I went into the house and told her. She did not believe it. I told her again: "It's over, I no longer care for you, I'm used to living without you." Finally she understood. I shall spare you the details of the scene. She told me some home-truths, spoke for example about my limitless pride to which everything was sacrificed. It wasn't entirely true, everything is more complicated.'

'But it was more or less true. You brought her back merely to let her go, to satisfy your self-esteem. But, what then?'

'I had to do it to free myself, do you understand? Anyway, when I won her back I was sincere, had no thought of forsaking her afterwards. At least . . . All interpretations are possible. To continue . . . 4 February exploded then. I was in the secret organization and managed to go to the Congo. Leli meanwhile was looking for me, trying to get me back. She fled from Luanda in April. She was trying to reach the Congo. She was captured by UPA and murdered. I don't know if I told you that she was of mixed blood . . .'

123

'Meaning . . .'

'Don't say it! I was the cause of her death, isn't that what you were going to say? Yes, I was the cause of her death. Unwillingly, but what does that matter? Leli alive could not manage to win me back. But her revenge was her death. It linked me fatally to her, in a feeling that is in no way love, but which has trapped me. Today I cannot love any woman, for fear of doing her harm. When I'm attracted to someone, boom! there is a glass between us, it is a fear of feeling again what I felt when I learned of Leli's death. Killing is not difficult, Commissar. It is nothing to kill in war!'

The Commissar weighed his words.

'That will pass when you meet the right woman.'

'I met so many! I left for Europe in 1962. There I knew so many students, slept with so many students! In '64 I returned to the struggle. I met so many girls! Nothing broke the spell of Leli. Perhaps I have become too hard, the certainty is that there is a barrier. That is the story. I still have the scars, but you can have the experiences. That's why I'm giving you the lessons I learned from it.'

The Commissar gave a silent nod.

'I understood, first of all, that a real man, one who cannot be dominated, is one who can cool a passion to follow a plan coldly. All feeling makes him irrational and, therefore, incapable of action. That any dominator is in part dominated, this is the dialectical relationship between the slave and the slave owner. That human relations are always contradictory and none are perfect. That fate smiles on the one who seeks it, through danger. That there are no gratuitous acts and that gratuitous courage does not exist, it must always be linked to the search for a target. And that, when someone wants to do something stupid, you should let him do that stupid thing. Let anyone crack his head, as he wishes! After his head is cracked, he is more willing to take advice. A plan can only be proved wrong when it does not achieve the desired objective.'

'One might say that your whole life has led you to military strategy, Fearless. The seminary, love . . .'

'Yes. Life shaped me for war. Life or I myself? Difficult to know.'

'Do you think about Leli a lot?'

'Yes. Before an action. And that gives me strength to fight.'

'Is that why you struggle?'

Fearless looked at him. Then he turned his gaze back to the water that, again, was running over his feet.

'No, I don't think so. I was already in the struggle before. There is never a single reason that leads a fellow to struggle. That had an effect, perhaps, but is not the sole reason. But don't you criticize me? Doesn't the story shock you?'

'Now no. Later perhaps, who knows?'

Fearless undressed. Nearby was a huge rock that went into the water. Beside the rock, the river was as deep as a man's height, which provided a natural swimming pool seven metres long by three metres wide. Fearless plunged in and remained submerged until he was out of breath. He came to the surface and made a few strokes to the edge of the pool. He plunged again, across the pool under water and came out close to the Commissar.

'You should have a swim.'

'And who would stand guard?'

'Right. When I finish, I'll stand guard.'

The Commander dived again. The water was fresh, almost cold. In Mayombe it is always crystal-clear, as it comes from mountain streams that run over stones. Fearless swam from one side to the other, until he felt cold. He came out shivering and looked for a ray of sun.

'Your turn. I'll stand guard now.'

'No,' the Commissar said. 'I've just finished eating.'

'Theories! Never harmed anyone. Colds are caught only by those afraid of them.'

'It's silly to die of a cold.'

'It's silly to die! But if I tell you that it does no harm ... Don't think about it and dive in. You'll see that nothing will happen.'

'Not worth it.'

Fearless shrugged his shoulders. He was still shivering, but his body was beginning to dry.

'There's one thing you haven't explained, Commander. If I understood properly, Leli always liked you. So how did she convince herself that she cared for the other man?'

'Love is like that. If it becomes reciprocal, passion disappears. One

125

needs constantly to revive passion. I did not know that yet, allowed myself to be persuaded by the quiet life we were leading. Can you imagine the life of an office worker in Luanda? It was good that I had the secret work, Leli began to take an interest, we studied Marxism together. But in feelings we had halted. We had reached stability. It was my fault that I adjusted to the situation, that I did not realize routine is love's worst enemy. Even in bed we had become routine. Then the other man came along, with aspirations as a poet, writing her verses, talking sweetly. He touched her sentimental side. Any woman likes to be a poet's muse. She showed me the poems later. They were detestable, but they moved Leli. She never had a strong critical faculty, it must be said. And he used mean tricks: he knew me better than I him. In conversations he would go on to Leli about how I was, or rather my bad side. Only after they were living together did I know him well. One must know one's enemy the better to destroy him.'

'And you didn't give him a hiding?'

'What for? I took Leli from him when I wanted. Do you want a greater revenge than that?'

A flock of large birds settled in a tree nearby. They were quacking like ducks. Fearless picked up a weapon. Then he shrugged his shoulders: there was already food at the Base.

'The first period of your separation must have been hard.'

'Yes. Things don't go in a straight line. I had crises of anguish, mixed with moments of apathy. All my work suffered. At night I used to think of her in the arms of the other man. So I made an effort to sleep, to convince myself that I was the stronger, able to control all feeling. I fell asleep with exhaustion. Sometimes I felt an urge to beg her to come back. But in front of her I maintained a stony aloofness, a sphinx. That was the name I gave myself, Sphinx. It became my nom de guerre, until they gave me the nickname of Fearless, I don't know why. Sphinx suited me better.'

The Commissar saw Fearless mastering the desert, taking the buffeting from the sand without blinking an eyelid. Everything happened inside, in the convulsions of stone, in the currents of air whistling through tunnels carved by time, in the slow wasting of seemingly stable matter.

'The contrary of life is immobility,' Fearless said. 'In love it is the same thing. If someone reveals himself totally to another, the interest of discovery disappears. What counts in love is the discovery of the partner, of faults, of defects, of vices, of grandeurs, of sensitive points, everything that goes into the other's make-up. The lover who wants to be loved should dole out this discovery. He should not want to know everything at once, nor reveal everything at once. It must be carefully measured out. And the human soul is so rich, so complex, that this discovery can last a lifetime. I knew a fellow, a militant, who on getting together with a woman made an honest self-criticism of what he was. He spent a night talking. He described everything as he saw it. "Now you know me, you have been warned." At the end of a month, the woman left him. And he was the best type in the world. His downfall was applying to the letter in love what he had learned in the Party about the benefits of self-criticism.'

'That depends on the women. There are women who want to know exactly what the man is like, to adjust to him, to shape their behaviour to that of the husband.'

'They are slaves. They are not looking for love, with all its risks, but for a quiet life. For me they are not women, they are rabbits. I'm not talking about those. I am talking about the ones who are serious opponents, who are therefore able to give the greatest pleasure and the greatest sorrow to a man. A characterless woman, who lives as a reflection of another person, submissively, is like a man who escapes misfortune without reacting. Mediocrities!'

'They are the result of society,' the Commissar said.

'I knew a woman like that. She was married, her husband left her, I think because she had turned herself into a doormat he was tired of wiping his feet on. It was in Europe. She had been separated from her husband for four months. I had known her earlier, she had a fairly exciting body, the chance came, I took advantage. She readily accepted kisses and caresses, but didn't want to go to bed. She was still hoping that her husband would come back and didn't want to betray him, even at a time of separation. If she went to bed with me it was because she was really in need of a man, it is one of the things that someone grows used to, even if it is banal. I took three hours to persuade her.'

'A great struggle . . .'

127

'You can't imagine! It was necessary to make her relive the moments of separation from her husband, to make her see her husband in the arms of another woman, to set her crying, then for the caresses to warm up until she was ready to lose her head. That night I was excited, she had attractive legs, if not I would have given up. No, it wasn't that! It was more the bet I had with myself and the curiosity of finding out what she was really like. After making love, she began to cry, saying that she was no longer worthy of her husband, that she was a tart, etc. Submission had totally shaped her spirit. I never wanted anything more to do with her, obviously.'

'That comes from the social role of women,' the Commmissar said. 'In a society where man controls the means of production, where it is the husband who works and brings the money home, it is natural for the wife to submit to masculine supremacy. Her social protection is submission in the family.'

'That's broadly true. But there are women who do not submit, who find in love the counterbalance to this social inferiority. And even without working, being economically dependent, they are able to match the man's game. Moreover it's their best protection.'

'They are exceptions. Note the centuries of submission. That leaves its mark.'

'You are right. But the woman I knew, and many others after all, was from a socialist country.'

'That doesn't mean anything, Commander. Firstly, this problem is not yet settled in the socialist countries. Secondly, it must be the last superstructure to be changed. It is the most difficult to change, as it clashes with all the moral and individual prejudices that previous modes of production have aroused.'

Fearless had dried off. Gazing at the river, he put on his uniform.

The Commissar had put his own problem aside for later, was calmer. Oh, it was still in waiting for later! When night came he would feel it as he turned in bed. But at this moment the despair had left him, which was better than nothing. They stood up and set off for Base, without speaking.

◆

They left the Base at seven in the morning, with three other guerrillas. Half an hour later they climbed the Shut-your-Mouth, a mountain that with allowance for some rest took two hours to climb, and where the ground was always slippery from the constant humidity. The mountain's name had been chosen by one of the first resupply groups, when the Base was being established in the interior. It was a group made up of civilians. One of them, at the mountain summit, began to cry, saying that he could not go on. Another told him: 'Shut your mouth, stop crying, who ordered you to join the Revolution?' All kinds of landmarks had anecdotal names. A tree trunk where a civilian had collapsed, refusing to go on, was 'Nuno's tree'; a slope where a little girl had slipped was 'Helena's slope'; a stream where Ngandu had fallen while crossing the log was 'Ngandu's stream'. They were names that recorded the scant prowess of the civilians from Dolisie. The guerrillas always pointed the landmarks out and took delight in using the names. It was also a help in exchanging information.

They conquered the Shut-your-Mouth and plunged into the high grass that whipped their faces and got into their clothes, causing an itch. They were already in the Congo. Angola appeared behind them in the shape of mountains covered in forest, with the summit lost in the clouds.

After they arrived at Dolisie at two o'clock, the Commissar set off for the school and Fearless went to the office. In the office he found the veteran Kandimba, who told him there was no lunch. What about the officials? Andre had not appeared and the representative of the leadership who had come from Brazzaville had gone out.

'Find me a scrap of bread, old man. I haven't had lunch yet.'

The old Kandimba brought him half a roll. Fearless ate it by the door, with an eye on the street. He had changed his uniform for civilian dress, but had not bathed in the guerrilla transit house, at the entrance to the town. He would do so at the office, after eating the bread.

'So now you are messing about with other people's wives?' Kandimba said.

'You?'

'Yes, you, the Kikongos.'

'That's rich here!' Fearless said.

He finished the bread and went to take a bath. Kandimba passed him a towel.

'It's bad,' the old man said. 'Comrade Andre did well to run away, or he'd have caught a bullet.'

'It's what he deserved,' Fearless said.

'Do you think so?'

'Why not?'

The old man nodded. He took back the soaked towel and nodded again. He pointed to the packet of cigarettes that poked out of a pocket of the shirt thrown across a chair.

'May I take one?'

'Take, old man. Doesn't Andre give you any money?'

'That one? Phew!'

They heard a car stop in front of the office. The old man ran out of the bathroom. Fearless finished dressing and went to the office. There he found a representative of the leadership and a crestfallen Andre, divested of all the aristocratic bearing his skinny body and long beard gave. Fearless greeted the leader.

'When did you arrive from Base?'

'Just now. Has the man finally shown up?' Fearless said, indicating Andre with his chin.

'Aren't you greeting me?' Andre asked.

'You? Just with a smack!'

The leader looked at the old Kandimba, who was witnessing the scene. The latter, without a word, left the office.

'He was hidden in a house. It was a job to persuade him to come here.'

'They'll kill me, I know they'll kill me.'

'The Commissar came with me,' Fearless said.

Andre trembled. He rose from the chair, grasped the leader's arm.

'Let me go away. They'll kill me. It's a disgrace for the Movement, let me go away.'

'You seemed braver when you faced the women,' Fearless said.

'No-one will do anything,' the leader said. 'You, comrade will stay in your room, with militants at the door to protect you. And only for the time the inquiry takes, then you will proceed to Brazzaville.'

'The guards will be just the ones to kill me.'

'Leave off squawking like a chicken,' Fearless said. 'If they do kill you, that's no great loss.'

'Enough, Fearless!' the leader said.

The Commander left the office. It pained him to see men frightened of death: a traitor's behaviour. And was this the all-powerful master of Dolisie? The veneer always falls when danger scratches it.

Andre went to his room, escorted by two armed guerrillas. The leader sent for Fearless. The latter sat in front of the desk.

'The worst is over,' the leadership representative said. 'When I arrived, the atmosphere was explosive. Yesterday we held a militants' meeting, where everything was explained. Accusations rained down. Not only this incident, but corruption, lack of interest in the struggle, tribalism. No-one dared defend Andre.'

'All the accusations are true, how can they defend him? But do not delude yourself. He has his backing.'

'I know. Tribal backing.'

'Obviously! Everything here is like that.'

'Don't think it's just here,' the leader said. 'In the other Regions it's the same thing. Tribalism is an objective phenomenon that exists everywhere. The odd thing is ... I don't know! Take a group that might be tribalist here, separate them and spread them in another Region. They will be the first to complain against tribalism.'

'They are in a minority,' Fearless said. 'Here we see that those comrades who are isolated, as the only ones from their area here, those then affect to be detribalised. I say advisedly, "affect," since I do not know if when they returned to their area of origin, where they would be in the majority, they might not revert to tribalism.'

'So, the majority tend to be more tribalist, isn't that so? Majority, but not only that, it's enough if there is a group, albeit a minority. The group builds up the ancient tribal solidarity.'

'That's it,' Fearless said. 'The idea would be for each individual to be isolated for so many years, in the midst of another group, to lose his tribal feelings. At the end of a certain period, I believe, he really would begin to lose them.'

'That's what urbanization does partly. It's a sad process, but it has

131

the merit of gradually eliminating tribalism. But, even so, it is a slow process.'

'All these processes are slow. Look at Europe and the question of national minorities. Even today it is not settled . . .'

'But the Europeans like to throw our tribalism in our faces,' the leader said.

'For them, what happens in Europe is not tribalism. All right, there are no tribes, the name is inappropriate. But it is a very similar phenomenon. Sometimes I am in despair here. Will we ever overcome this evil?'

'Don't doubt it. But it will take a lot of work. And types like Andre don't help overcome it.'

'Yes,' Fearless said, 'they just strengthen it. What puzzles me is that this scandal should be necessary before an incompetent official is dealt with. Without knowing what was happening, we were on the point of marching on Dolisie to arrest him, because we were dying of hunger and food was not arriving. For four days we had only "commons" to eat. And that is nothing new. The leadership must have known, why did it let the situation rot?'

'There were no concrete facts.'

'There were no concrete facts? How many reports were sent to inform you? We had to wait for woman trouble to settle the matter.'

The leader offered cigarettes.

'Fearless, listen. There are things that cannot be done in the air. We read the reports, received letters, but that was not enough. There had to be a deed . . .'

'Always that. When a man goes around with a pistol and shouting that he is going to kill another man, no-one does anything. He has to shoot before steps are taken.'

'There are other matters to settle. Things are not simple.'

'Things are never simple, comrade,' Fearless said. 'And they become more complicated as time passes.'

'I understand that for you things must be done quickly, you want to advance the war, for sure. And you do not take other factors into account, or you underestimate them. But we are often forced to go slower than is desirable . . . Anyway, that's a matter for discussion, but I have not had lunch yet . . .'

'Nor I,' Fearless said.

'You've come from the Base and not eaten?'

'No, Kandimba said there wasn't anything.'

'Now this! Kandimba! Kandimba!'

The old man appeared at the door almost instantly.

'So you didn't give comrade Commander any lunch?'

The old man scratched his head.

'You comrade told me to keep lunch, I kept it. But you did not tell me to give it to other people.'

'So a person comes from Base, tired out, and you don't give him food? That's not right. Let's go to lunch then, Fearless.'

They rose and went to the room at the side. The old man served them. When the old man went out, the leader said:

'I don't understand what's going on here.'

'I am Kikongo and he is Kimbundu. At this moment that factor counts, is the basis of anyone's reactions, as Andre is Kikongo. It wasn't he who committed the error, it was the Kikongos!'

'And mixed up with bureaucracy. He didn't give because I told him to keep food!'

'Bureaucracy is the defence,' Fearless said. 'He took refuge in bureaucracy, that was the heart of the matter. However, he knew how to beg me for a cigarette . . .'

'We have to find a replacement for Andre,' the leader said.

'Shouldn't be difficult.'

'Hum! It isn't so easy. There are a whole range of things to consider.'

'Has Ondine already been heard?' Fearless asked.

'Yes.'

'Has she asked for a transfer?'

'It's the only thing to do.'

'I don't know,' Fearless said. 'Things may still be sorted out with the Commissar. At least that is what he thinks. In this case, might be better to wipe the slate.'

'I don't believe so. The leadership will see. But such incidents, in the Movement, always require a punishment. Even if it means suspension.'

'Yes, the eternal Christian morality!' Fearless said.

133

'Revolutionary morality, comrade.'

'Leave off! Revolutionary morality, nothing. It would be revolutionary morality, if all the cases were penalized or none were. There is a series of similar incidents, everyone knows, and nothing is done. Only when it causes scandal does the Movement interfere. That is Christian morality, interested in appearances. Moreover, I think that a case like this is not a crime against the Movement, it is human. In Ondine's case. In Andre's no, because he is in charge.'

'You don't change, Fearless.'

'And will come to a bad end for it, I know.'

They ate in silence for a while. It was fish stew. Kandimba brought a bottle of palm-wine and filled their glasses.

'When did you last have a drink, Fearless?'

'Some four months ago.'

'Anyone who had seen you in Europe would never believe you would put up with that. I haven't forgotten one meeting with the students when you appeared blind-drunk.'

'Don't talk nonsense. I drank too much, yes, but I could cope. When I felt I had had too much, I went to bed.'

'Prudent behaviour!'

'I got used to that in Luanda,' Fearless said. 'A drinking bout is dangerous for anyone doing secret work, as he might talk. It was good training.'

'Generally, when a person drinks, he becomes honest.'

'I too. But only to myself. It is dangerous to be honest with other people. So, when I reach the threshold that will make me honest with other people, I go to bed, lose all sensation, go into a coma.'

They had finished the stew and palm-wine. They smoked in silence, observing each other.

'How is the Commissar?' the leader asked.

'Depressed.'

'That will pass.'

'These things leave their mark. I was afraid that he would do something stupid, but no, he's calm.'

'All the better! He's a chap who could go far.'

'Yes, he could go far,' Fearless said.

'He mustn't do anything stupid.'

'He won't.'

'You watch over him, don't you?'

'I do what I can.'

'I've heard it said that you are like a father to him.'

Fearless smiled. He drew a deep breath.

'If there was anything I've never had it was paternal instincts. But that might be as good a way as any to label my attitude.'

'He could get on. He is disciplined, good fighter, good political training. He must not do anything stupid. But to change the subject ... It is a good thing that you have come, as someone must stay here. As soon as the inquiry is over, I shall go to Brazza with Andre. Perhaps by tomorrow. Until the new official comes, you must take care of Dolisie. Don't object. There's no escaping it, it is necessary. I promise you that it won't be more than a week.'

'Which is the same as saying a month.'

'No, it will be quick. We know that you will be needed in the interior for this advance.'

'We were going to carry out a series of actions. All the plans crashed. First they were delayed for lack of food. Now because of what happened. If I have to stay longer, then ... One must take into account that at this moment the Commissar is unable to shoulder alone all the responsibilities. As soon as the kicking out has been done, then it will be easier.'

'You're only staying for a week.'

'But put someone capable here. It's time to have competent people in charge here. Not this gang of bureaucrats who put themselves in key positions and sabotage everything.'

'The better ones are in the guerrilla war,' the leader said. 'Would you agree with taking cadres from the guerrilla war?'

'In the last resort. But only in the last resort. There are some talented lads there: New World, Theory ... With a little more running in, they will make excellent cadres. Above all political cadres. Among the soldiers, we have promising material: Muatianvua, the Operations Chief, Miracle, Truth ... They are the best fighters.'

'Do you think that New World would do for Dolisie?'

Fearless lowered his eyes. Thoughtfully, he finished the cigarette.

'New World is tough. I should like to have him in the guerrilla fighting longer to know if he is really tough or if it is merely a cover. But he seems tough to me. He is decisive, has good training, has knowledge of organization, is dynamic. And he was in the guerrilla war, so he knows its problems and needs.'

'So would you agree for him to come here?'

'The difficulty is that it is a sudden promotion. I was thinking of appointing him a group chief, to start with. Wouldn't such a jump be harmful? From a simple guerrilla fighter to being in charge of Dolisie . . . Might spoil him. Although I don't think it likely, yes, he is solid.'

'Do you have any objection to him?'

'I don't like him much, as a person. He is a dogmatist! But this is personal, has nothing to do with the rest. He might not be my friend, but he could be a good official at this stage, and, who knows? If in the future . . . And we need new blood. He is capable of good work, I'm sure of that. And a fish learns to swim by living in the water. Guerrilla warfare may be too narrow a context for him.'

'The fact of this . . . don't know what to call it . . . incompatibility of temperaments between you, will not cause difficulties between the Base and rear-guard?'

'No, I don't believe so. There are no reasons for that. Why don't the 21st century and the 20th century unite against the 19th century?'

'When he arrived,' the leader said, 'I noticed his toughness. I think you're right, he is tough. Let's consider this hypothesis. The jump is sudden, but it was in the logic of things.'

'He could organize the rear-guard well. And without a firm rear-guard, nothing will be done.'

They rose from the table. Kandimba came to fetch the plates. They leaned on the veranda.

'All that's missing is a good coffee and brandy,' Fearless said.

'Coffee can be arranged. Not brandy, as we are in a financial crisis.'

'As always!'

'What do you expect? So long as we do not rely essentially on our own strength, that's how it will be. The people don't give support, nor can we collect real subscriptions. Everything has to come from abroad. Kandimba, make some coffee, please. About New World: what do you call being dogmatic?'

136

'Being dogmatic? You know as well as I do.'

'It depends, words are relative.'

Fearless grinned.

'You're right, words are relative. He is too strict in his notion of discipline, does not see the current conditions, wants to apply the scheme as he learned it. That I call dogmatic, I think it is the true meaning of the word. His truth is absolute and ready-made, refuses to admit any doubt, even for the sake of discussing and strengthening it with evidence in practice. Like the Catholics who refuse to doubt the existence of God, because that might worry them.'

'And you, Fearless? Aren't your ideas absolute?'

'Every man has a tendency towards that, especially if he has had a religious upbringing. Often I have to make an effort to avoid swallowing as universal truth some particular observation. A person is accustomed not to argue, not to call into question a series of lessons that have come to him from childhood. One needs constant attention not to fall into facility, not to be caught by the label in front and so run away from a profound analysis of the reality. Since schematism, labelling are the effect of intellectual idleness. Intellectual idleness or lack of culture. But it is the former that is serious. Obviously it is also an evasion.'

'Do you know something, Fearless? You are an intellectual.'

'We are.'

'I don't say that in a pejorative sense. You are in fact an intellectual. And I think it is a good thing for you to be. Perhaps you have an over-critical attitude, you are doubtless marked by the Region, by failures, by mistakes. In other Regions it isn't like that. If you were in another Region, then you would change your attitude a little, you would see that things are not so bad, you gain a wider perspective. And I think it won't be long now.'

'Am I going to be transferred?'

'It's under consideration. But keep that between us, for the time being. Does the idea appeal to you?'

Fearless remained silent for a while. He contemplated the street, the occasional passers-by who ventured into the sun, he eyed the leader.

'It certainly appeals to me. I am fed up with settling trivial problems. I like to wage war and there's no war here. It's exhausting to struggle without the people. On the other hand, I must tell you that I like this Region and that it has potential. The fault is ours, we have not been able to make the most of it. But, if they were to give me a choice, I would rather go to another Region. Particularly if it were a new Region.'

'To open a new Front?'

'Yes. The Chela mountain, for example. Or Huambo.'

'It is the pioneering spirit speaking! That wouldn't be a complex in you?'

'I don't understand what you mean.'

'Have you ever taken a girl's virginity?' the leader asked.

'No, never had that.'

'That's what I meant. Until you do that, you will always want to open new fronts.'

Fearless gave a roar of laughter. The other laughed as well.

'Freud doesn't explain everything.'

'But he explains a lot,' the leader said.

'It's odd!'

'What?'

'It's odd,' Fearless said, 'here we are discussing Freud, when we are faced with great political confusion, with adultery and almost a revolt in the middle. It is the vice of intellectuals, this taste for talk in any circumstances.'

'No, the people of the village are still worse. And note that that was an aside, we were still dealing with real events. We were just talking about your transfer . . .'

'You are acquitted, comrade! But is it a serious thing?'

'Most certainly. The difficulty is finding a replacement. Clearly it is not immediate, it will take a good three months. But meanwhile things here will progress a little, I hope. I did not come with this mission, but you should soon be contacted by the leadership for your view. Although you may think the contrary, there are certain steps we do not take without consulting those affected. When that is possible, obviously. The suggestion came from the East, we here must give our recommendation. Your wish will be realized, since they need a Commander to advance beyond the areas currently at war. Where, I don't know, that is a military secret. But it is for a new Region.'

Fearless's eyes brightened. He sensed in his nostrils the wind of the highlands he had known in his youth. He saw the majestic slopes of Tundavala, where the world opened to beget the Namib desert: Tundavala was the half-opened thighs of the mountain that let flow the sands of the desert, flooding the horizon as far as South Africa. He sensed the fragrance of eucalyptus in the mountains of Lepi, remembered the maize fields of Bie and Huambo, the scarlet flags of the acacias in Chongoroi, everything leading down to where the earth died and the slaves in the past lost their future for ever. He saw Benguela, the ancient storehouse for slaves, the fattening yard for blacks, like cattle, awaiting the ship for America. There the path to America opened, but for the black man the path to life closed. Now, Benguela would not be the premature graveyard for the New World, but an open door for a new World. Fearless's eyes sensuously ran down the steep slopes of Huila or the gentle slopes of Huambo and revelled, in dalliance with the sea, and in the spray confusing the lonely silhouettes of the baobabs or the architectural hairstyles of the highlands women.

'It would be heavenly,' he whispered.

He had seen it all as a tourist, from the top of passenger buses, arrogant in his view from above and in his pretensions as a young man from Luanda. He would follow the same circuit, now on foot, with his household on his back, a snail wielding a weapon, perhaps no longer identified with the expression of the majestic baobab, but with the mulberry tree of Mayombe, whose roots entwined with the verbena or the almond trees, in a vital embrace.

'For the time being your place is still here,' the leader cut in.

'Which does not stop me dreaming about the future.'

'As long as the dream does not interfere with your faculties for the present, it is not prohibited.'

'It will not interfere with them. I am not a passive dreamer. Dreaming leads me to create the future.'

'Rubbish! It's a long time since I saw you so optimistic, so sure of yourself.'

'You have given me the first good news I've heard in years.'

'Is this coffee coming or not?' the leadership representative shouted.

139

'It's being planted,' Fearless said. 'In this Region everything takes time to grow.'

The coffee arrived finally. They drank it in silence.

'I'm going to the school,' Fearless said. 'I have to look out for the Commissar, keep an eye on him, as you say. Heavens, that's the man who could replace me.'

'I had thought of him too. But perhaps he would be too young.'

'What is this fear of the young? You remind me of all those fogeys who fear the competition from the younger generation. All right, see you soon. Now I am going to see to my paternal duties.'

◆

People avoided him. Or when they could not do that, they greeted him without really knowing what to say. A scab, he thought. A cuckold, to give things their right name.

Ondine was in her room. He knocked and the reply followed swiftly. He went in. Ondine looked at him, took the hand he held out to her.

'It would have been better if you hadn't come.'

'I received your letter. I had to talk to you.'

'Why, Joao? There's nothing to talk about.'

He sat on the bed. They avoided each other's gaze. But in a flash he had time to notice the deep dark rings round the girl's eyes. She sat on a bench, with her hands between her thighs.

'I must know. I think I have the right to an explanation.'

'It's useless.'

'I must know.'

'That's masochism.'

'Not in the least. So far I haven't understood why. I want to know where we fell down. Don't you think it's my right?'

Ondine nodded. For the first time, she looked straight at him. He could not sustain the gaze.

'Is it your right? I don't know. The problem isn't one of rights or duties. But I think this is only rubbing salt in the wound to no purpose. We are just going to be hurt, to no real purpose. It would have been better if I had left before we met. It's over. Each goes his own way.'

'No.'

Ondine raised an arm and then despondently let it drop.

'All right. What do you want to know?'

'How did it happen?'

'How did it happen? Do you want the details?'

'Everything.'

'Joao, that's masochism.'

'Perhaps, but I don't care. What is masochism? I want to understand. It isn't enough for me to accept without understanding, it's the same as not accepting.'

'Well. About a week ago perhaps, I met Andre on the road to Dolisie. He stopped the jeep, offered me a lift. I accepted. We went to a bar, we drank a beer. We came back to school. It was growing dark. He stopped the jeep in the middle of the road.'

'And then?'

'Then we went into the bush.'

'Is that all?'

'What more do you want to know?'

'You wouldn't go into the bush just like that, I know you.'

'Do you know me, Joao?'

He didn't answer. She stared at him, saw that his hands were twisting. 'Well, if you must know . . . In the jeep he kissed me. When he suggested that we go into the bush, I agreed.'

'Why did you let him kiss you? Why did you agree?'

'I don't know. I felt like it.'

'But why? That doesn't happen by chance.'

'With me it may happen by chance. It depends on circumstances, it depends on the man . . . That's just how I felt, Andre is a fine man.'

'So you didn't care for me?'

'Who knows? There are several kinds of love. Anyway, that doesn't matter any more. I am going away and you will find another woman.'

'No, that doesn't interest me. No woman will interest me. Never again!'

'Heavens! That's childish. Have you thought how it would be if we hadn't been spotted? A militant saw the jeep abandoned on the road,

141

suspected something was wrong, you know how they were spying on Andre to get rid of him. He saw us return to the jeep.'

'If you hadn't been spotted . . .'

Ondine paused for a few seconds of silence. She made the same weary gesture.

'I would have written to you just the same. It was that night I wrote the letter you received, even before I knew that the incident had been discovered. No, I couldn't have hidden it from you.'

'But earlier, Ondine? Had you ever had anything to do with Andre?'

'No. He pleased me as a man, that was all.'

'And after this, have you come to care for him?'

'No. It ended there.'

The Commissar stood up and grasped her hands.

'Ondine, there is nothing lost. I don't mind.'

'No, Joao, it isn't worth it.'

'If you liked him, then it would be different. Like that it's not important. You were alone, you were angry at the way I went away, the opportunity presented itself. Yes, I know, that was it. It was a thoughtless gesture. I don't mind!'

'You say this now, Joao. After the complaints and charges that have been made.'

'I shan't say any more about it.'

'Even if you don't say anything, you will not be able to forget about it. Every time you go away, you will be suspicious. You will always be expecting another letter. I don't have the right to keep you in that situation.'

He tried to embrace her. She gently pushed him away.

'You would remember all the bad and never forgive me. Our relations would be based on jealousy, love, and a desire for vengeance. We would be walking a tightrope. Until, one day, you would cast in my face what happened.'

'Never!'

'That's what you say now.'

'I love you, Ondine.'

'Maybe. Sure, you do. That's just what complicates matters. Everything would be so easy . . . We could still go on being good friends.'

'Either lovers or enemies. Between us friendship is impossible.'

142

'I know, it's a pity.'

The Commissar tried again to embrace her. Ondine let herself be hugged. He stroked her hair, kissed her throat. When he sought her lips, she broke away.

'No, Joao, it's useless. I don't want you, you understand? When will you understand that once and for all? I don't want you, I don't love you any more.'

Her changed tone enraged the Commissar.

'It's not true! I know it's not true.'

The Commissar embraced her violently, squeezed her close to him. She tried to escape but he used his strength. He kissed her on the lips, almost biting. Ondine moaned. He caressed her violently, then threw her onto the bed.

'Better not, Joao.'

Clothes went flying as he tugged. He stripped rapidly, controlling her, as she struggled.

'I'm going to show you that you care for me.'

He was brutal, without caring whether she would enjoy it. Ondine remained lying, eyes closed, thighs in the same position, when he rose from the bed abruptly, already remorseful. He sank down at her feet and sobbed softly. She stirred from her torpor and stroked his head. The Commissar lay down again, his head on her breast, and wept. Until his sobs again stiffened Ondine's nipples and he felt this. The love-making was less brutal, the second time round.

'We'll be heard,' she said as they broke apart.

'What does it matter to me? What does it matter to you? Tell me that you are staying with me.'

'I can tell you that now, Joao, but what is that worth said in bed, after love-making? Tomorrow, in cold blood, I might tell you the opposite.'

'No. You will say the same thing.'

'Now I would agree to remain. Because for the first time we really understand each other. But it will be the same again later and I shall desire other men.'

'Tell me that you want me.'

'Yes, Joao. But tomorrow . . .'

'What does tomorrow matter to me?'

Again they entwined. Night fell outside and the room was dark.

Fearless waited a long while at the school and in the end returned alone to Dolisie.

The Commissar did not appear in Dolisie until much later, when the Commander had already gone to bed. Joao went to speak to him in his room.

'It's all arranged, Fearless. She's staying with me.'

Fearless saw that the Commissar's shining eyes were seeking approval in his.

'What do you think, Commander?'

'You're the one who knows. If you see that things can be worked out, all the better for you. I am very happy. What happened may not be important . . .'

'That's it. It was a momentary impulse. It isn't important, Fearless.'

'For you is it really unimportant, Joao?'

The Commissar lowered eyes that had instantly clouded over. He soon raised them. The shining light had gone out.

'I will do my best, Fearless. I will have to get used to the idea gradually.'

You will not be able to, Fearless thought. Perhaps the next time you will already be sufficiently detached and unprejudiced. But now it is too soon. I was a year younger than you, see what happened. I too tried to wipe the slate clean, perhaps in less dramatic circumstances. Or more dramatic perhaps, who can compare the incomparable? Ondine is not Leli, Ondine is dominant, Leli was submissive. The difficulty does not lie in Ondine, and that makes it worse. The difficulty lay in me, and lies in you. You too want to free yourself, to have the last word. Is that really it? Perhaps there is true love, love that overcomes self-esteem. Could it really exist? It existed in Leli, at the end, when she tried to win me back. A passing phase, until she found another man. The truth is that she had not found another man merely for lack of time. In Joao, could it really exist?

'How did you persuade her? Since I imagine she wasn't willing.'

'By force. I as good as raped her. Then she agreed.'

And the rest, Joao? Sex was at the end, but before? Will it be the end? It is the basis, could easily be the starting-point. Who knows where the end is or the beginning of the circumference? Love is a

144

circumference, whose centre is sex, perhaps that might be more accurate. And when all's said that is nothing. Who can define love, who can express it in geometry?

'You should talk to her, Fearless.'

'Perhaps.'

No-one who interferes between a man and a woman ever settles anything, but rather complicates it. But I cannot tell you that, Joao. How can one say: do not believe in good fairies? How can I tell you that if I tried to stick you together I would perhaps be the acid that in the end corroded your fragile links? The matter must be between you two, never accept an adviser between a couple, Joao. How can I tell you? How many homes have been destroyed by third parties in the guise of sorcerer's apprentice? Destroyed when they had their foundations in ruins. That is your case, Joao. It always is the case when one has to seek the help of third parties. Rot has already eaten away the foundations, glue will serve no purpose, one must demolish in order to build from scratch. Yes, but how to tell you that?

'You must be the one to settle it, Joao.'

'You're my friend, you could help, Fearless.'

'No. Let everyone crack his head as he knows best!'

'Are you abandoning me?'

'You've already settled the matter. Is it the best solution? How should I know? Only you two can tell.'

It is the cigarette that feeds the habit, by claiming to be the last. Why not give up smoking once and for all? Fear of leaping into the abyss. We cling desperately to fragile roots, merely prolonging the inevitable. Jump, Joao, leave go of the root and jump into the abyss. At the bottom there may be water to break your fall. You are not afraid of danger, Joao. How can I tell you? What right have I to tell you? What is true for some may not be true for others. Ondine will not love you, have you still not grasped that, Joao? You were told that today, you were offered that last cigarette. But the break with dependence starts tomorrow. Face it today. How to tell him that? How to say it without killing him? Get rid of the poison once and for all, you are strong enough to bear up, you do not have to cut down the habit gradually. Free yourself, Joao, leap into the abyss, refuse the last cigarette.

The Commander said nothing. The Commissar went sulkily off to bed. The two of them lay awake, but did not speak to each other.

I, THE NARRATOR, AM ANDRE.

Here am I on a train, on the Brazzaville route, on the banishment route, seated in front of a man who does not reply except in monosyllables, serious as befits a representative of the leadership. His briefcase goes along with him, locked up, full of documents that must compromise me. It is enough to look at his face to know that the hearing will go against me.

And where are my companions who failed to defend me? They all ran away, not one dared open his mouth in my favour. All those who used to flatter me, who hung around me in hope of a crumb, they ran away in fear of the Kimbundus. There's no doubt that it's the Kimbundus who make the rules. Didn't they manage to free Ungrateful? Now I want to see how Fearless will settle the matter. He succeeded in what he wanted. He was always after my job, that's why he pulled strings, stirred up the Kikongos against me, went so far as to come from Base when he found out what was happening, just to be on the spot, the better to bury me.

I laugh when I think of the leadership representative's face, when he learned of Ungrateful's escape from prison. We were at the station with Fearless: the leader gave Fearless a hard look. Would he have known that Fearless did not want him executed? Must have known, they always know everything. Fearless was speechless. Now he will have to settle the case, which is complicated, as he must take action against the Kimbundus, just now when tribal feeling is running high. At the Base he drew back: for fear of this conflict, he was merciful, knowing perfectly well in Dolisie Ungrateful would escape. Let us laugh, let us have a good laugh. He did all he could to take my place, he always wanted to remain in the rear-guard, his fighting spirit was just fireworks. Now you have my place, you will find out what thorns are hidden on the climb, my cousin.

Who would be fooled by the plot that was mounting against me? They did not have facts to latch onto, Fearless and his group. So they planned Ondine's coup. I am paying for my imprudence, for my credulity. Did I desire Ondine? Yes, long since. Her thighs were a temptation. Her eyes were promising, were not lowered. When I saw her on the road, I had

146

nothing in mind. It was in the bar that the feeling came. It was beginning to grow dark. Why not? She looked at me challengingly. And then, in the jeep, her thighs opening . . . I looked at her and she stared back at me. She saw that I was goggling at her thighs and she took advantage of a jolt by the car to spread them wider, imperceptibly but it was enough. I stopped the jeep, who wouldn't have? A man is not made of straw! Was it I who kissed her or did she make the first move? The tart soon agreed to go into the bush. What fire, my god! What a volcano! I lost my job, but it was worth it. They'd put a string of militants in ambush along the road, to provide witnesses. And she lent herself to the plot, because she is a cow who likes a man and because that way her Commissar will be promoted. Fearless will move to the post he sought and who will be the new Base Commander? Obviously it will be the Commissar.

It was all a plan contrived by Fearless, there can be no doubt. It was simple for him to persuade the Commissar, who does just what the Commander wants and is ambitious. As easy as falling off a log! I was trapped, but I had my own back. What moments! And she enjoyed it, the bitch! She would not stop, wanted more, always more, and didn't even feel the mosquitoes biting her bum. When she went back to the jeep, she could scarcely walk, she was so whacked. And she took the chance of a man. Since it's not that kid of a Commissar who will give her satisfaction, that's easy to see. It was a plan in which she sought a double benefit. The Commissar would have wanted her merely to go into the bush and then refuse and run back to the jeep. That would have been enough to dish me. That must have been the plan. But the bitch wanted to play her role too. And what a role! She was zealous, women are always like that, they must change a plan to their advantage, if fifteen minutes are enough, they delay for two hours.

And this wooden-head didn't see anything. Who would believe in the plot? No-one. It isn't even worth the trouble to expose it, no-one would believe. They would think it was an excuse.

Anyway, I'm wasting time. The worst is over. In Brazzaville they won't eliminate me. I've still got my supporters. Not those types who didn't dare defend me even, not that mob. I have well-placed supporters, people of influence. I shall do my self-criticism just to disarm my opponents and this will provide the opportunity for my friends to plead my cause.

Lenin was right to invent self-criticism. What a fine thing self-criticism is!

There are some dunces who always refuse it. They haven't yet found the loophole. When you're in a jam, make your self-criticism. All attacks will stop at once. It is the theory of action and reaction: a force causing an action produces a reaction, there must be a reaction to be performed. If you cut out the reaction, which in this instance would be your defence, what happens? The action ceases to be performed. As easy as falling off a log. I shall begin my self-criticism right from the start, then the attacks will be merely a matter of form, and will already have lost all their venom. Who can attack a man who is not defending himself? They will regard me as a good militant, since I have made self-criticism. And they will not demote me, just post me elsewhere.

Only dunces are obstinate, keep themselves in the wrong. Since I made mistakes, why deny it? I should have been wary of Ondine and taken her away to a secluded spot, where there could not have been any witnesses. It would have been talked about but there wouldn't have been evidence. And she would have fallen in with it, she was already aroused: the plan would fail, but at least she could still play a role. Another mistake was to trust some of the militants. The mob are all the same, unworthy of trust, the official counts for them only when he can bring them benefits. That is why my father, as village chief, wasted so much money in handouts to his men. He knew only too well that if he did not do so he would lose his strength. My mistake was to forget these elementary lessons.

Basically, basically, the one who will be trapped is Fearless. I shall go to another posting where I shall get on just the same: there is such a shortage of cadres that the one-eyed man is king. He will stay here with all the problems, that will now be worse. Fearless is just a fox cub, but I am an old fox, and know what I'm talking about.

I must prepare my self-criticism, it must sound sincere. To sadden myself at the time, I shall be thinking that I could have enjoyed a week with Ondine and not just those two hours of bush and mosquitoes. Easy as falling off a log!

On the morning after, Fearless went to accompany the leader and Andre to the train. He had been put in charge of Dolisie provisionally, until the definitive appointment had been made. The Commissar had set off for the school. The leader had given instructions for Ondine to stay at the office building, until her case was settled. The Commissar went to help her move her things.

At the station they learned of Ungrateful Tuga's escape. The leader eyed the Commander.

'This concerns one of your guerrillas. You must settle it immediately.'

'Yes,' Fearless said.

The train started, disappeared round a bend. Fearless felt alone. He had never liked seeing people off, preferred to be the one going away. Above all at the present moment, it would have been useful for the leader to have stayed longer. But the inquiry was complete and he had to go and explain the occurrence to the rest of the leadership.

Fearless jumped into the jeep. Hungo sat beside him. What he wanted was a drink of beer. He set out on the road to the prison.

'How did Ungrateful escape?'

Hungo made a vague gesture.

'In the morning they saw he was missing.'

'Who was on guard?'

'I don't know.'

The Commander lit a cigarette. To do this he had to leave go of the wheel and duck down out of the wind. He thought of making a detour to the school to pick up the Commissar. He would be a useful adviser, at this juncture. But he abandoned the notion: the Commissar was unable to think of any other problem than his own.

The prison was a small block at the armoury, guarded by a few guerrillas. Fearless leaped down from the jeep and showed the service order that put him in charge of Dolisie.

'Well, comrade Commander,' the Stores Chief said, 'what do you want from us?'

'Who was guarding Ungrateful?'

'There were two on at night: first Kill-All, and next Katanga.'

'On the gate?'

'Tranquil and Angelo, the one who recently deserted from the tuga.'

'You put a newly-arrived deserter on guard?'

'Shortage of manpower.'

'That's no good, it's a mistake, you don't know who he is. He might be sent by the tuga as a saboteur.'

149

'Yes, comrade Commander.'

All Kimbundu, except the deserter, Fearless thought.

The guards were called for questioning. Their answers were identical: they had not heard anything, no sir they had not slept, they had not noticed anything unusual. The guards on the gate might not be implicated, Ungrateful could easily have escaped through the hedgerow, without passing the gate. But, as for the prison guards, one of the two must have opened the door for him or let him do it. The guard remained at the door only at night, and did not go and check if the prisoner was sleeping inside. So, one of them might be innocent.

Fearless ordered them on parade. When the guerrillas were lined up and the Stores Chief had reported the parade, the Commander said:

'Kill-All and Katanga are going to prison. One of them helped Ungrateful to escape. They will serve his sentence, until it is clear exactly what happened.'

The guerrillas hesitated to carry out the order.

'Comrade Chief, choose two guerrillas to lock up Kill-All and Katanga. And if one of them escapes, the Stores Chief will be held responsible.'

The Chief made a sign to two guerrillas, who reluctantly complied with the order. There was a murmuring in the line.

'Stop talking,' Fearless said. 'I know what you are thinking. But take it easy, this will all be finally sorted out by the new appointee. Until he comes, or until the true culprit is detected, I am obliged to order the arrest of the two comrades. One of them was to blame, but how can one find out?'

The muttering did not stop.

'Comrades, I knew there would be agitation, I was expecting it. They will lay this at comrade Andre's door too. In this case he has nothing to do with it, as you know as well as I. Let us speak frankly! Ungrateful is Kimbundu, the majority of you are too. Some rascal took advantage of the confusion in Dolisie to free him. They thought no steps would be taken since, as Andre is Kikongo and has committed offences, no-one would dare to take action against a Kimbundu. So I am taking it! I do not care if someone is Kikongo or Kimbundu. I am against what he does wrong. It cannot be denied that I was against Andre, as he made many deliberate mistakes. And he is almost a relative. All of you here know me. Only the blind or the wilful can say that I practise tribalism. And you know that I am not afraid of tribal blackmail. Comrade Stores Chief is responsible for the two prisoners. Until one of them speaks up, confesses and says that the other had nothing to do with it. Then the innocent man will be freed immediately.'

Fearless left for Dolisie, with the feeling of general hostility behind him. Hungo muttered, when the Commander could no longer hear the guerrilla's comment:

'This Commander is a man!'

The Stores Chief nodded in agreement, but the other guerrillas were still complaining of arbitrary action.

Fearless was driving, absent-mindedly. They are used to things being delayed, for an inquiry to be held and a decision to follow. In the time that took, the guilty party would already be far away. They must understand that Andre's cowardly methods are over, at least while I am around.

The Commander found the Commissar at the office. He soon noticed the hangdog look.

'Where's Ondine?'

'Already in the room.'

'What's up with you?'

'We argued. She doesn't want me after all. You must go and talk to her, Fearless. Please! You're the only one who can convince her. Don't abandon me, please.'

The Commander did not reply, but went to the room assigned for Ondine. It was across from Andre's room, which he must now occupy. He knocked on the door and went in. Ondine was sitting on the bed, with her hands between her thighs. She looked up at him.

'Hullo, Ondine. We haven't seen each other yet.'

'No.'

'Joao has just spoken to me. He says that you don't want anything more to do with him.'

She shrugged her shoulders.

'Would it be very impertinent to ask for a cigarette? Now I can smoke as I please. I used to avoid doing so to avoid shocking people.

They took my little ones away, I am no longer trusted to teach them. So I can smoke as I please, it doesn't matter any longer.'

Fearless lit her cigarette. She took a draw.

'Joao doesn't understand or doesn't want to understand. I know him. Now he accepts the matter readily, his behaviour is admirable. That's what makes it complicated, that he has these admirable traits. It's difficult to refuse him anything, he is so down-hearted, such a child! He accepts now. But tomorrow he will begin to blame me. That is not the difficulty. The difficulty is that it won't work between the two of us. I am more mature than he. I would tend to dominate him. The same thing will happen again and he will be willing to accept it. It's not fair!'

The Commander lit a cigarette for himself. He too sat on the bed.

'If I understand correctly,' he said, 'you think there is an imbalance between you that works in your favour.'

'That's right.'

'And you don't accept the situation.'

'I know myself. I know that I will exploit his weakness. Because he is weak. I don't want to abuse anyone, least of all him. I need to meet a man who does not let himself be dominated. I respect him too much to abuse him. And I shall always be bound by that.'

Fearless watched her silently. He had thought she wore only the mask of a liberated woman, made by herself. After all he was mistaken.

'Joao is not a weakling, believe me. He doesn't have much experience, that's all. Who knows if this might not make him more mature?'

'Surely,' she said. 'If we break up, that could temper him. If we go on together, this will merely scar him without leading him to surpass himself.'

'And if he had to struggle to win you back?'

'There's no time. I shall be gone soon, don't understand even why they have left me still in Dolisie.'

'The tactic of the Movement in situations such as this is to send each party to a different place,' Fearless said. 'But only after all possibilities of reconciliation have been exhausted. That's in the case of married couples. In your case, as you are not yet married, I don't know . . .'

152

'Fearless, forgive me for calling you that but it is easier,' she held his arm. 'You understand me?'

He nodded.

'Don't you think it's better this way? That I am not the wife for Joao?'

Fearless sighed. Then he said:

'That's the crux of it. You are in fact the wife for him, and Joao knows it. Not for the Joao you knew, but for the Joao you have made germinate, who is being born.'

'It would take time.'

'It would, yes.'

'And it would need me to love him.'

'In other circumstances, outside war, it might be possible. The blight is that he must be far away, will not have the chance to show himself off in the new skin he is making, and that you have helped him make. It is a sad and slow metamorphosis.'

She did not respond. Fearless, as he left the room, gently closed the door. Now he must face the Commissar. With a sigh, he went into the office.

'Well?'

What to say? How to put it? How to sweeten the vinegar?

'Nothing doing, Joao. She has her reasons. You will understand later. One day you will see that it's better like this. I wanted to tell you yesterday, but I wasn't quite certain.'

The Commissar once again let himself flop down on the chair. He rested his head on the desk. Fearless went and closed the entrance door, so that no-one should see him crying.

The sobs gradually tailed off. Until the Commissar raised his head.

'Your discussion was so quick . . . So you did nothing to persuade her, isn't that so?'

What was the truth? Had he done anything to persuade her? Yes and no. Persuade her of what? Of what truth?

'No, I did nothing. She has her reasons, I agree with her.'

The Commissar looked at him in silence. Tears were still trickling down, but the sobbing had stopped.

'One day you too will understand. Nothing is possible between you. Nothing serious, permanent. Perhaps later. Later, yes, if you meet again. But you shouldn't even think about that, you should free yourself.'

'So you told her she was right? So you reinforced her view?'

Did I reinforce her view? Perhaps. Always yes or no, when one does not know the path to follow.

'She already had her view.'

'But you didn't try and persuade her of the opposite?'

'No.'

'You told her that she had done right even.'

'If I didn't say it, that was what I meant. I don't know if I told her that, but it was what I meant.'

The Commissar stood up. His lips were quavering. Violently he gripped the edge of the desk.

'You betrayed me, Fearless. You betrayed me.'

'But what do you really want? Do you want Ondine at any price, or do you want a serious relationship with Ondine? What do you really want, Joao?'

'I want Ondine, haven't you understood yet?'

'Whatever the consequences?'

'Yes.'

'Then I betrayed you, Joao. I betrayed you. Because that was not what I thought was for the best. If it was to have Ondine at any price, without it mattering to you what could happen to you in the future, you should not have asked me to go and talk to her. I would not have gone.'

'Know what you really are, Fearless? You are jealous. I begin to wonder if you are not homosexual. You wanted me to be alone, like you. A hermit of Mayombe. Because you would have me to yourself alone, my protector, my godfather. You drove Ondine from me. You never wanted to advise me, I asked you several times. You never wanted to talk to her and you could have persuaded her. You never wanted to interfere to sort things out between us. You wanted me on my own and for that you let me be a wash-out. See what you have done with your egoism. See what you have done. Now I am a cuckold, a mat on which to wipe one's feet, a mat everyone uses. Are you happy, Fearless, are you happy?'

The blow from Fearless sent him reeling against the opposite wall.

The Commissar raised himself slowly, rubbing his face. His eyes glittered.

'Have a care, Fearless! I am not going to struggle with you, and that is what your anger demands. I despise you. I am not going to struggle with you, I am not giving you that trust. Think of it as fear, if you like, I don't care, you are already so mistaken about me it is just one more. You think you have eliminated me, that you have driven my love from me. But I shall not be a loner like you. You will never see me behind an empty bottle. With Ondine or without Ondine. Good-bye, Fearless, till the next time. You will see what I shall turn into. Every success I score will be a repayment for your slap, as I shall not be a failure like you.'

He went out, banging the door. Shaking, Fearless let himself down into a chair. He lit a cigarette greedily, as if every draw was the last. Idiot, little idiot! The cigarette was finished. Papers were piled up in front of him. With a gesture, he swept clear the desk. He stood up and moved into the sitting room. Idiot, little idiot!

He left the office and went quickly on foot to the nearest bar. He sat at a corner table and ordered a beer. He drained it from the bottle and ordered another. He filled a glass. No, no he would not get drunk like a child. He emptied the glass at one go. He refilled it. Love! Love drives one to folly. His hand burned with the force of the slap. It was the same hand as held the glass. He emptied it again. He ordered another bottle. The girl asked for money. He paid for the three beers. She brought the bottle. She is afraid I shall get drunk and not have any money to pay. No, I shall not drink any more. He emptied a first glass, then filled it again. It would be the last. He had stopped shaking, his hand now held the glass steadily. The very cold beer brought on a nervous pain. Was it the beer or this kid? He, Fearless, had always settled his romantic entanglements alone. Since his time at the Seminary, where he could not trust his colleagues, always prompt to denounce others in the secret of the confessional. The Commissar had threatened him. With what? That he would begin to settle his personal problems on his own.

He felt what was coming, but could not avoid it. The burst of laughter filled the empty bar, scattered the flies that were soaking up the drops of beer on the tables, made the serving girl turn round. The girl saw him holding his sides, laughing until tears came. Then she shrugged her shoulders and went on washing glasses.

Fearless stopped laughing, and only the tears glistened. The kid had finally shown his claws. And he, Fearless, had not understood, had gone so far as to slap him. He had castigated the words and lost sight of the words' meaning. At last, he sighed. At last! And I did not understand him, remained dazzled by the words. And I am the one who always says that words are relative . . .

He emptied the glass and rose from the table smiling. As he passed the serving girl, he greeted her with a stroke of her buttocks. She bore with it, with a shrug.

On his return to the office, Fearless almost bumped into Ondine, who was going out in a frightened manner.

'What's up?' he asked.

'Where were you?'

'I went across there. But what's up?'

'Joao, Joao has gone mad.'

'How? Calm down, calm down, Ondine!'

He took her back to the office and closed the door. He sat at the desk.

'He is crazy!'

'But what happened, damn it! Tell me once and for all!'

Ondine sought to control herself. Her voice began uncertainly, but gradually gained confidence.

'He went to my room, I think when he left here. He opened the door without knocking. He began to talk, saying that you and I were mistaken about him, that he would not let himself be beaten. That we wanted to destroy him, to crush him, that we had taken advantage of his innocence. That I thought he was a child, that I did everything to destroy him, but he was not a child and would not let himself be destroyed. That he was going to show what he could do. So, he did not want anything more to do with me, was ridding himself of me, was going to forget me at once. And you had always tried to prevent me from loving him, or, at least, had not helped. That you wanted . . .'

'Him to be a hermit like I am,' Fearless said.

'That's it.'

'He made the same speech to me. And then?'

156

'Then he undressed me. Yesterday he tore one of my dresses, today he tore the other. He undressed me by force, but did not try to touch me. He told me: "See I can be with you naked there and not have the desire to make love to you!" He told me this was the first time that had happened and proved he was cured.'

'And you?'

'I? Did not even open my mouth. Then he said that he was going to show he was as good a soldier as you, that you had created a myth that he was going to destroy, by proving you were no magician to give orders.'

'He's right.'

'That he had allowed himself to believe that you were an exceptional man in all fields, but were nothing after all.'

'He's right.'

'That you had created this myth yourself, out of vanity. That you pretended to take great risks, but were always calculating the risks. You fooled others, as you appeared to risk everything, when after all you put yourself in safe positions.'

'There he exaggerates!'

'That he did, really, risk everything, without any tricks. And so he would show that what you do is just to deceive.'

'As long as he doesn't do anything silly . . .'

Why does a man's affirmation always have to be in opposition to all others? thought Fearless. Why this constant struggle for life, struggle for position, or struggle for prestige? Such is the original sin, not spoken of by the Church, but spoken of by Marx.

'He said too that he was leaving at once for the Base. You would stay on in charge here, he would go and command the Base.'

'It's the natural order of things! The Commissar automatically stands in for the Commander. But was he leaving immediately?'

'Yes.'

Fearless's first impulse was to grab the jeep to stop him. It was late, he would have to travel in the dark and possibly on his own, it was not wise. But then he let himself fall back into the chair. I go on reacting like a father. He is breaking out.

'I don't think he's mad at all,' Fearless said. 'His reactions are almost normal. A little hasty, as quick decisions always are. You shouldn't worry about what he says, he says no matter what, tomorrow it will have passed. What you should do is note his behaviour. I had told you he was turning into a man, a while ago you saw that it is true.'

'But his behaviour is infantile . . .'

'To outward appearances perhaps. But the decision is not. How can you expect him to react in an entirely mature way, in form and content? One can't, it's too soon. It is a profound revolution. The form is still infantile, you could say, but the form will change later. The form is behaviour, the content is the motive for behaviour.'

Ondine sceptically put out her lower lip.

'You think so?'

'At least there is a dialectic. He may fall back, certainly will in some regards. His maturity is brusque, violent, so will not be complete at once. But he is on the way. I already have a replacement, I hope better than I. Suppose we went to lunch?'

'You aren't worried, Fearless? You aren't shocked by what he said about you? You can take it so calmly?'

'How do you want me to take it?'

'He insulted you.'

'Heavens! It was never an insult to break a myth. He was the one to create a myth around me, now he realizes he was mistaken. Perhaps I helped him create this myth, who knows? It was not my intention, but I may have played a part. He realized of his own accord and now, on the road, with every step he will destroy the idol he made. There is no reason at all to be worried or offended. From now on, he will not need myths to survive, he will become a free man. We should be happy.'

'I don't understand you, Fearless.'

'You're not the only one. Sometimes I have difficulty understanding myself. But c'est comme ça! Let's go and eat, all this has given me an appetite.'

'I'm not eating, I can't eat.'

'Christian behaviour. The stomach has nothing to do with problems.'

'I'm too nervous.'

Ondine went thoughtfully to her room. Fearless went to eat.

158

Next morning an old man asked to speak to the person in charge. They showed him into the office. The old man was an MPLA militant from the frontier. He was startled to see Fearless.

'Don't be disturbed, old man! Comrade Andre was transferred, I'm here in the meantime. What can I do?'

'Comrade Commander, I came to inform you that the tuga have set up a camp at Fallen Branch.'

'At Fallen Branch?'

'Yes. They were seen by some hunters going into the interior. A big camp.'

Fallen Branch was an old guerrilla base, abandoned some three years earlier. The tuga wanted to control the frontier, from there they could easily monitor entries and exists. And they were a day's march from the Base, with almost a direct route.

'When did they see them?'

'Before yesterday. I came here yesterday. On the way I met comrade Commissar, yesterday afternoon.'

'Did you inform him?'

'Yes. He said it was all right.'

'Didn't he tell you to inform me?'

'No. He just said it was all right. I came because I was already close, I'm taking the chance to buy some things in Dolisie.'

The Commissar already wanted to take on responsibility alone, thought Fearless. It was what he must do. He bade good-bye to the old man and sent a jeep for the Stores Chief to be fetched urgently. While he was waiting, he was dealing with minor matters for the militants in Dolisie. But his thoughts were far away. Tuga in Fallen Branch was bad news. Soon they would discover the Base. Moreover they could cut off the resupply route from there, since the entry into Angola was not adequately camouflaged and was a promising target for attack. And that fellow Joao going off alone and angry! They will know what to do there, I do not have to worry myself.

The Stores Chief arrived, came into the office and slumped into a chair.

'What's wrong, comrade?'

'What's wrong? I didn't sleep last night.'

'Why, are you ill?' Fearless asked.

The Stores Chief was a burly man, looking about forty. He sighed.

'Those prisoners! I had to stay on guard all night.'

'Why? Aren't there any men to do guard?'

'There are. But I don't trust them. Just two or three I can trust. The rest would let the prisoners escape, for sure.'

'You know your men well, comrade Chief!'

'I know them, yes.'

Fearless smiled: the Stores Chief was Kimbundu.

'That's not why I called you. They've just come to tell me that the tuga are in Fallen Branch.'

'Is that right?'

'Yes, seems so. Do you know what that means?'

'I know, yes, comrade Commander. Dangerous!'

'Steps must be taken. Stores is on stand-by. No-one goes out. Have the weapons cleaned.'

'All right. Out there are militants who could handle a weapon, as reinforcement.'

'Give me a list of them,' Fearless requested.

'I'll send it over, comrade Commander. At any moment they might attack the Base.'

'Or set an ambush on the frontier or at Shut-your-Mouth. I don't know if they will send a group over there from the Base, we must think about that here in Dolisie. They are short of guerrillas at the Base, it's here where there's no shortage.'

'You can count on us, comrade Commander, to do our best. Dangerous, very dangerous.'

'Yes, it is dangerous,' Fearless said.

'About the prisoners?' the Stores Chief asked.

'Put on guard the men you trust and go to sleep. They stay like that, until the new man in charge arrives.'

The Stores Chief went out and Ondine came in.

'Are you very busy?'

'Yes.'

'About me, what have you decided?'

'I? Nothing. I'm waiting for instructions.'

'Haven't you made a report on Joao's decision?'

'I don't make reports about personal matters.'

160

'But it isn't personal, Fearless. You could indicate that Joao has accepted a separation. There would no longer be any need for the leadership to delay my departure.'

'Do you want to leave, Ondine?'

'What am I doing here? At least let them punish me and send me to the East!'

'Wait a few more days. At least you brighten up the house!'

'I didn't think you were so gallant, Fearless. Tell me. Doesn't my delay depend on you?'

'How, on me?'

'Aren't you the one who has to inform the leadership?'

'No. That is already in the hands of the leadership, I have nothing to do with it.'

'Good. May I at least go out of the office or am I a prisoner here?'

'You can go out as you please.'

'So, bye for now, Fearless.'

'Bye for now, Ondine.'

Fearless went on looking at her haunches as they moved away. He lit a cigarette and called the next militant in. It was a request for a pair of trousers.

Here am I now settling problems of a pair of trousers, he thought. I ended up badly, there is no doubt. The Commissar was right: a perfect failure. Let us hope they take all the security measures, and that Joao does nothing silly.

'He won't do that,' he said aloud.

'Sorry, comrade Commander?'

'Nothing, nothing, I was thinking of something else.'

Right, so now this man thinks I have gone mad. Anyway that is not far wrong: keeping me in this job for a month would be enough. How would Mayombe be? Green, as always.

I, THE NARRATOR, AM STORES CHIEF.

This is the second night I shall have no sleep because of the prisoners. If I sleep, they will escape.

I was a fighter in the First Region, served as guide to the groups who

161

went into Angola from the Congo or out to the Congo. I went into the interior again with the Kamy Squadron and after the debacle managed to get back. Sick, I stayed on to work at Stores. Up to now. My health does not permit me to be permanently at the war-front and I regret that. But taking care of military equipment is part of the revolution.

There in Quibaxe, I was already a grown man and married when the war began. A landless peasant, I used to work on a settler plantation. I joined the war, in the knowledge that anything I could do to put an end to exploitation was right. And I did everything possible. But it was not as quick as one might expect. Traitors prevented the struggle from growing. Traitors on all sides. It is a lie to say that it is the Kikongos, or the Kimbundus or the Umbundus or the mulattos who are traitors. I have seen them in all languages and all colours. I saw our own countrymen who had plantations take advantage in order to expand their plantations. And some collaborated with PIDE.

So, Fearless is right. So I do not sleep, in order that justice be done. Ungrateful committed a crime against the people and whoever helped him escape committed one as well. It is right that they be punished.

I am already old, I have already witnessed much. Words have value, the people believe in words as gods. But I have learned that words have value only when they correspond to what is done in practice.

Fearless speaks as he does. He is an honest man. What do I care about the language his ancestors spoke?

He is alone here in Dolisie. Surrounded by enemies, or at least by persons who do not understand him. The guerrillas respect him as Commander, but they mistrust him as a Kikongo. I respect him and do not mistrust him.

So I stay awake.

162

CHAPTER 4

The Snake

A day passed with nothing new. Fearless was expecting news from the frontier or from the Base. Another day passed and his anxiety decreased. Perhaps it was only a mistake by the hunters or the understandable exaggeration of rumour. Meanwhile, the Commander kept Stores on stand-by.

At dinner there was only Ondine: the other militants were held back at the Stores. They ate bread and drank tea, in silence.

'Still worried,' Ondine said.

She did not know anything and could not understand the comings and goings. Fearless shrugged his shoulders.

'I am fed up with being here. Just problems of money and indiscipline. The war is far from anyone's thoughts. In a Revolution, there are those who live for it and those who live on it. It might be said that they have brought together here all those who want to live on the Revolution. They are the ones who soak up most resources and most time.'

'Suppose we were to take a stroll? You could invite me out.'

'I can't. I might be needed on urgent business.'

'Andre wasn't bothered about that,' Ondine said. 'He went out whenever he felt like it.'

'Andre was a bureaucrat and saboteur. I should be grateful for you never to compare me with Andre.'

Ondine lowered her eyes at Fearless's sudden coldness. She whispered:

'I didn't mean to compare you with Andre, sorry.'

'We can't go out. But, if you like, we could go to the veranda to enjoy some fresh air.'

They went to the deserted and dark veranda. They sat on the cement floor, and gazed at the stars and the empty yards. Movement in the small town had ceased, except for the occasional passing pedestrian on the way to a bar.

'I never liked small towns,' Fearless said. 'Either big cities or bush. Small towns make me sick.'

'What you can't stand is working in an office.'

'That as well, obviously. But small towns, where everyone knows everything, make me sick.'

'Sometimes I think you ran away from your course, on the excuse of joining the struggle. I don't see you as an economist, seated at a desk. The other day I observed you. You were sitting at the desk and fidgeting all the time, like someone uncomfortably settled. As an economist, you would have been very unhappy . . .'

'It depends. There are economists who move about, who do not work in an office. You don't see me as an economist, how do you see me then?'

'A soldier.'

'Just that?'

'Yes, I see you just as a soldier.'

'So do I, Ondine. That's the difficulty. Because one day it will be necessary to give up weapons, there will no longer be any reason to wear uniform . . . Because I don't want to be in a regular army either.'

'So what will you do, when the war's over?'

'I don't know. That doesn't worry me. And you?'

'We are talking about you. I don't see you as a sailor either, that isn't your style. And you are not the kind of person to live on a pension and regale others with your feats of war.'

'In brief, I have no future. But that does not disturb me.'

'Meanwhile, you should be making plans. Don't you sometimes dream of the future?'

'Yes.'

'Of what?'

'Impossible things.'

'For example?'

'Heavens. That all men should cease to be stupid and begin to accept the ideas of others. That one could walk naked in the streets. That one could laugh at will, without anyone turning round and putting a finger to his head. That one could make love when one wanted, without thinking of consequences. Etc., etc. Impossible things, as you see.'

164

'Do you really think that?'

'If I tell you!'

Ondine smiled. She pointed out a drunkard staggering by.

'I would like so too. Meanwhile, I'm looking at that drunk. And in the street I would be able to turn around and laugh at him.'

'I too, Ondine. That is what infuriates me. We want to change the world and we are unable to change ourselves. We want to be free, to do our will, and all the time we find excuses to repress our desires. And the worst aspect is that we convince ourselves with our own excuses, stop seeing clearly. Just cowardice. It is a fear of facing ourselves, it is a fear that lingers on in us from the time when we feared God, or father or a teacher, always the same agent of repression. We are alienated. The slave was totally alienated. We are worse, because we alienate ourselves. There are chains that are already broken but we continue to carry them along with us, for fear of throwing them away and then feeling naked.'

'Today you were depressed, Fearless.'

'It's always like that when . . .'

'When what?'

'Nothing.'

Ondine stared at him. He withstood her gaze, but did not speak. She lowered her eyes. Fearless watched her at will. Ondine was in her customary position, head lowered towards the ground, hands between her thighs, which showed where the skirt had ridden up, and belly smoothly swelling. Was Ondine beautiful? Perhaps not, she had a hint of the unfinished girl as a woman. Her position, seated on the ground with legs folded, emphasized that aspect. He saw her hazily by the light from the street lamp. The silence that ensued erected a barrier between the two of them. She was the first to break the silence.

'You are a man, you could be much more free. If you want a woman, there is nothing stopping you.'

'Like you, it's the same.'

'No, society is much harder on the woman.'

'I wasn't talking about society, but of individual morality.'

Ondine laughed.

'It's priceless! You have an individual morality?'

'You're insulting me. Do you think me a fellow without morality?'

165

'We are talking about different things. On the sexual aspect, for example, does your morality sometimes prevent you from satisfying your desires?'

'But that's just what I was saying! A person is led into thinking of the consequences and controls his desires.'

'Do you?'

'Do you think I'm a sexual degenerate then?'

'No. A libertine.'

'Not even that. I knew a libertine. I knew a heap of people, should be a writer to describe them. It was in Prague, on holiday. A genuine libertine. No woman he found attractive would escape him, even if she were his own sister.'

'What happened to him?'

'Nothing. I don't know, probably went on like that. I am not a libertine. I was too marked by taboos to be such. At a certain moment, I did think that was the answer, did everything I could to build for myself a libertine philosophy. But I didn't succeed, failed rather, moral problems always cropped up to ruin everything. I had a lot of discussion with my friend in Prague and saw that there was a world between us. Or a generation at least .'

'Was he Czech?'

'No. French. A communist. Perhaps not communist in the classic, orthodox sense of the word, but in my sense.'

'In that women are collective?'

'What kind of an idea is that? That is Catholic anti-communist propaganda. In his view, any woman must be free to accept him or refuse him, just as he was free to desire any woman or not. Just that. And if there were consequences, each was free to put up with them. He was a communist, not in the sense that women are collective, but in the sense that they have the same freedom as men. As you see, it is a programme that fits on one hand.'

'There are fellows who are not communists and think like that.'

'I know, Ondine, that is not enough to make a communist. But he had all the rest. A bourgeois or a pseudo-revolutionary such as we are might think like that, but is never consistent to the extreme of his actions. He was the most free person I knew. I always envied him. Then I realized I could never be like him and I conformed. A man

166

must know his limits precisely and accept them. Otherwise he is a weakling who deludes himself about himself. Or dishonest.'

'But did he put his desires above the Revolution?'

'That was his tragedy, he told me. Sometimes he chanced to desire a woman and have urgent work, without the possibility of pursuing her. In that situation, he would choose the work.'

'Then he was not free.'

'No-one can be free when there is a Revolution to be made. But even so, he was the most free man I ever met, as only social or political factors could restrain him. They were not factors of individual morality, such as because so and so was married or because . . . of whatever. There are husbands who do not betray a wife simply because they do not like to be betrayed and have an awareness that freedom belongs to all equally. They are already advanced, but you must admit that they are still a long way from my libertine in Prague. And they are the most advanced in our society.'

'How would you handle that?'

'I? I would not marry, that's the easiest way.'

'You are dodging the question.'

'You are awake!' Fearless smiled at her with tenderness. 'You're right, I am dodging. I am going to be honest, for once in my life at least. I should hate it, could not even bear it, if my woman should sleep with another man. I know what that is, I've been through it once, could not do it again. However, I think that she should be as free as I to have her adventures. If we were to marry, what would happen? I would be faithful to her. Not because I would not desire other women, but in order to demand from her the same faithfulness. As you see, marriage would be a hypocritical cage. Therefore I do not marry. I have not yet reached, nor never will reach, the level of my Prague friend. For him that was natural, it was in the order of things.'

'Was he married then?'

'Yes, to an East German woman.'

'What was she like?'

'Like him. Do you mean what was she like physically? Very beautiful, really very beautiful. She had blue eyes that, sometimes, especially when the light struck them, flashed violet lightning.'

'Poet . . .'

167

'Some women bring out the poet in me.'

'Did you sleep with her?'

Fearless lit a cigarette. He saw Karin as if before him, a queen, challenging, poised, with legs striding, hands on hips, wry smile.

'No. I ran away from her. That's when I realized I could never be as my friend. She would entice me, flirt with me and I pretended not to notice. Why? Because she was the wife of my friend, who for his part was not bothered if I should sleep with her or not. He was even in favour! As you see, I am not a libertine.'

'He did not like her,' Ondine said.

'That's what my mother would say and my aunt, and my aunt's aunt . . . I am not as sure as you are. We reason in terms of our society, a society assimilated to the European Judaic-Christian culture, in which the husband must be jealous, because that is the scapegoat and the wife is his property. What happens essentially to property that is let to another? Sometimes it is renewed, rejuvenated, through the investment of capital and labour. But we do not realize this. A wife is special property. We are a generation behind. We, city people, who are black on the outside. Listen, a Congelese who caught his wife in the act in one of the villages, near the frontier, demanded recompense for the offence, obviously. A comrade asked him if he was not angry. He replied: why? That doesn't wear out the woman. That is the style of thinking of an African who has little contact with the Christian religion. We are acculturated, corrupted, much more alienated.'

'That is why you do not marry, Fearless? Because jealousy is alienation?'

'Today that is the main reason. Yesterday there might have been another. There are many reasons for such attitudes, it depends on the occasions and the discussion. In this regard no-one is ever honest. He merely reveals a motive, which totally distorts an interpretation of the matter. But enough talking about me. Let's talk about you.'

Ondine raised her arms and dropped them again.

'Give me a cigarette. In my case I am a libertine. I could perfectly well marry your libertine in Prague, we would make the perfect couple . . .'

168

'That's a lie! Just a while ago you were saying that he did not love his wife because he was not jealous.'

'You didn't let me finish. We would make a perfect couple, but who said anything about loving? For me, the perfect marriage is one where there is tenderness and the desire occasionally to be with the other. Love destroys marriages. I don't believe in love. I should marry only a man such as your friend, for whom I felt friendship and a certain physical attraction. But I have never met such a man.'

'I don't believe a single word,' Fearless said.

'At this moment that's how I feel.'

'Agreed. But yesterday you were not thinking that.'

'Oh! Yesterday, yes.'

'All right. But a month ago you were not thinking it.'

Ondine, shrugging her shoulders, said:

'You yourself said that one never tells the whole story. I can be jealous too, it depends on the situation. At the start of a relationship I am jealous. As time goes by, I stop being so. That means I am fed up with the person.'

'Aren't you jealous of Joao?'

'Why mention Joao, Fearless?'

'Because he is involved here.'

'Perhaps in relation to you. I had already forgotten him.'

'Liar!'

She repeated her gesture of raising her two stretched arms together.

'I had forgotten him. He was already so far away! But not for you? Basically, you are the one who should be his woman.'

'That's what he told me. He implied that he thought I might be homosexual . . .'

'You attach too much significance to his words.'

'You are a good student! You repeat to me what I spelled out to you the other day . . . That's why a person should not throw out dicta carelessly: they always rebound on the one who offered them.'

They smoked in silence. It was Ondine's turn now to observe Fearless, as he was lost in study of the stars. Was Fearless handsome? Yes, without doubt. He breathed strength, not physical, animal strength, but a controlled, desirable strength. His beard deepened the impression of a lion sleeping calmly, sure of himself. A bit too sure of

169

himself, that was what had irked her when they had first known each other. He had won her with the calmness of someone who is used to winning and attaches no importance to the victory. Beside him, Ondine felt herself a frightened urchin, with a need to be conspicuous to draw attention to herself. A challenge to him had become impossible, the duel was meaningless: Fearless was disinclined to it, not through fear, but through lack of interest in such a conquest. However, Ondine surmised that Fearless desired her and even felt some tenderness towards her.

Perhaps because he remained silent, far away in a world to which she was denied entry, Ondine said:

'A woman is afraid to love you, to take you to her . . . It is as if you always had your knapsack on your back, in readiness to escape.'

Fearless was touched by the complaint, because it was a whispered complaint. He turned to her.

'I've been told that before.'

'How many women have already fallen for you, Fearless? Those you know about and those who kept silent for fear of seeming ridiculous? How many wept, how many ran away before they fell into the net from which there is no returning?'

'I don't know, a few.'

'Thousands.'

'Why do you say that?'

'You are the kind of man that women go for. You pass by them, indifferent and haughty. Women are masochists, they like someone who treats them as expensive merchandise available for the purchaser's means. So you consider them . . .'

'Is that a declaration of love?'

'No.'

'Oh good! Otherwise I would already have fled!'

Ondine laughed against her will. Always humour to put a stop to a conversation that was becoming perilous. Ondine understood that Fearless's humour was a defence. It was at that moment that desire really gripped her, an uncontrollable desire that made her cross her legs and squeeze her sex with her thighs. Fearless eyed her. She turned her gaze away. But she swallowed saliva and he received the message. He allowed himself slowly to be infused with her desire, as his own grew with it. Then he took her by the arm and drew her to him. Ondine offered her lips and he drank in their thirst.

'Let's go to my room,' he said.

Ondine stood up and followed him, squeezing her thighs to avoid shouting out. The corridor was empty and they went into the room. She was about to undress impatiently, but Fearless stopped her with a sign. He embraced her. They kissed each other slowly. Only then did he lead her to the bed.

In the middle of the night, they lit cigarettes.

'Does anyone come in here?' she asked.

'No. If by chance anyone does knock at the door, I'll put you behind it. But no-one will come in.'

'It would look bad if they knew. Not for me, my reputation is already established. But you . . .'

'It would only matter to me because of Joao.'

'Why?'

'It wouldn't be very pleasant for him to know.'

'But he's already finished with me!'

'And later on? Do you think he killed love and jealousy in one day? He will start thinking it was all a ploy of mine to be with you. Think that stupid, if you like, but that's how it is. Just imagine what a person imagines when he is alone and thinking that the object of his love is with another man! Do you think he's not still tossing in bed, thinking of you?'

'Don't talk about him.'

Ondine was almost shouting. She is not as immune to him as she would like to appear, thought Fearless. He was not surprised by the observation. Ondine was a volcano, all the elements of nature unloosed by a legendary hero. Fearless now knew why the Commissar had failed. Too late to help him.

'You never had any pleasure with him.'

'Why do you want to know?'

'I wasn't asking,' Fearless said. 'I was stating it, so you don't need to respond.'

Ondine threw her cigarette away. She raised herself in the bed and presented her young bosom to him. Fearless lightly bit her nipples and she twisted round in surrender. He moved away.

171

'Why don't you come close?' she said.

'I haven't finished my cigarette yet.'

'You are hateful!'

He smiled. He stroked her thighs with his free hand and she squeezed his hand. Fearless let the hand lie and went on smoking.

'We never got on well. He controlled himself too much, or controlled me too much, I don't know. The certainty is that he was always absent, worried . . . tense.'

'That's where it all went wrong.'

'Except the last time. When he took me by force, it was wonderful. He was violent, passionate, demanding, vengeful, without concern for the pleasure he was arousing in the partner. Why wasn't he like that before, Fearless?'

'He had not yet been whipped . . . He could not be like that before. He learned through failure. If it was a failure! It is now. Yes, now it is a failure, since you don't want anything to do with him. But you could try to start again.'

'The past is not wiped out, Fearless.'

'You could help him to wipe out the past, gradually he would forget.'

'But I am like this, I enjoy knowing new men. Later I would want another man. Basically, it would not be for the man as such, but for the attraction of novelty.'

'You like discovery, don't you? You enjoy the dangers of the first steps, the cautious struggle that leads to the final approach, the surrender so full of hesitation at the start that leads to the total surrender. Isn't that it?'

'Exactly. How do you know?'

'It's natural. That's a passing thing. I think it is a phase in the development of personality. I remained in that phase. It is the infantile side, incomplete. Or perhaps that is what love is. A man is attracted to what frightens him. The sea, desert, the abyss, the concept of God, death, lightning . . . To face another person for the first time is frightening, so it attracts the adventurous. However there are couples who find true pleasure only long after their first love. One cannot lay down universal laws.'

Fearless finished his cigarette. He put it out in the ash-tray and Ondine stretched out over him. He accepted her.

They began smoking again later. Fearless turned on the radio to the government station. It was playing Angolan music.

'With you, yes, I would stay,' Ondine said. 'With you I would live.'

Fearless allowed himself to be hugged. She stroked his hair, kissed his beard, his eyes.

'With you I would stay, Fearless.'

He nodded his head. He kissed her.

'No, Ondine. You did not accept the Commissar because he submitted to you. With me, it would be the opposite: you would submit to me.'

'Yes, I don't mind. It's what I need. A strong man who dominates me. I feel like a wild animal that must be tamed. Tamed animals are most faithful to their master!'

'I don't want to dominate anyone.'

He was about to say: I do not need to dominate anyone, but he changed the wording in time. Ondine snuggled up to him and murmured:

'Perhaps I should tame you as well.'

'When I felt that, I would leave at once. So it isn't worth trying. Let us remain with this night, which has been unforgettable. Why spoil everything, trying for an unattainable continuity? Some things are made to be unique, such as tonight.'

◆

They were woken by frantic banging on the door. Ondine, swathed in a sheet, ran behind the door. Fearless, as he slipped on his trousers, shouted outside:

'What is it?'

'The Base has been invaded!' came the shout.

'What?'

'The Base has been invaded!'

'What Base?'

'The Base, your Base, comrade Commander.'

Fearless, in the confusion of putting on his trousers, forgot Ondine

173

and opened the door. VW was on the other side, exhausted. The Commander was half in and half out of his twisted trousers, and was struggling nervously to sort them out. VW did not notice.

'The Base, Commander, the Base . . .'

Ondine hid behind the now open door. Fearless went to look for his boots under the bed. VW came in, Fearless did not stop him.

'Find me those damned boots . . . The Base, you said . . . How come?'

VW squatted down to hunt for the boots. As he turned, Fearless saw the looming white sheet and remembered Ondine.

'Come, let's go outside. First tell me how it happened.'

And he hauled VW out of the room.

'The tuga attacked.'

'And the Commissar?'

'I don't know. I was by the oven, heard the bursts, saw the comrades running, running away, I went to my hut to fetch the pistol I'd left there. The comrades were running to the spot where the enemy was.'

'Wait, then you can tell the story. Go and call Kandimba. I'm just coming, must find my boots.'

He went back into the room. Ondine was sitting on the bed. Fearless searched for his boots, slipped them on, put on a uniform shirt, slung his cartridge-belt around his waist and picked up the AK.

'I'm going to fetch people from Stores.'

'What are you going to do?' Ondine asked.

'Go to the Base. Salvage what we can.'

Ondine squeezed his hands. Her eyes glistened with tears.

'Suppose Joao were captured?'

Fearless shrugged.

'You must rescue him, Fearless. You must rescue him. For tonight, for me, you must do it.'

'So you care for him after all!'

Ondine sank down, sobbing, on the bed.

'If anything happened to him . . . Oh, if anything happened to him, it's my fault . . .'

'Rubbish! Was it you who took the tuga there? I am going to rescue him, if possible.'

Fearless kissed her on the nape of her neck and, carefully closing the door, went out. The mist in front of his eyes had cleared. In the jeep, which roared off at a hundred towards the Stores, VW told the rest of the story.

'Comrade Commissar brought news that the tuga were in Fallen Branch. A group was sent to patrol the mountain in front of Fallen Branch. The enemy had already advanced, since they attacked us.'

'Who was leading the group?'

'The Operations Chief.'

'Go on.'

'The Commissar ordered the guard to be strengthened and we dug trenches. It was then I heard the bursts and the shouts of "take him alive, take him alive!" I didn't know what to do, I remembered that I had left my pistol in my room, went to fetch it. My clothes I could leave, but not the pistol. Then I saw comrades running, all in a line. But they were going in the direction of the shots. They must have been confused.'

'And the Commissar?'

'I didn't see him. I remembered the guard on the other flank and went to warn him. He was already advancing towards the Base. He came with me and we retreated through the mountain.'

'What do you think happened to the rest?'

'They were running to where the enemy was . . .'

There was an element in the story that puzzled Fearless. But his thinking was not clear.

'From what side did they attack?'

'By the river.'

'Just by the river?'

'The shots came just from there.'

The tuga is not so stupid! To attack a base from one flank only? And how is it that Muatianvua or Truth, or the Commissar even, should run in the direction of the shots, if they had the mountain open? Fearless stopped thinking about this as he arrived at the Stores.

He entered with a roar, hooted, shouted. The men, half-asleep, struggled to their feet and picked up weapons. The Stores Chief also appeared, still dressing.

'The Base has been attacked,' Fearless shouted. 'Go with the lorry and collect all the civilians who can shoot. I'll take the guerrillas in the jeep. Meet us at the office.'

The lorry started out almost immediately. Fearless remained with the guerrillas, choosing weapons for the civilians. They loaded ammunition on to the jeep and the two light machine guns. When this operation was complete, the jeep started out for the office. The lorry was already there, full of men. They jumped down from the vehicle and surrounded the Commander's jeep.

'We are going to try to reach the Base,' Fearless said. 'I want volunteers only. Anyone who is afraid should not board the lorry, it isn't worth it. The Base has been attacked, we don't know what is happening to our comrades. No-one who does not want to go is obliged to do so. Those who do want to go should come and collect weapons and ammunition.'

All the men put out their hands for weapons. The Stores Chief distributed them.

'Comrades, the MPLA has men!' Fearless said.

He jumped from the jeep and went into the office, to hide his feelings. He met Ondine on the way. She gripped his hands.

'Promise me you'll do everything possible.'

'I've already promised that, Ondine.'

'Thank you.'

Fearless gave various instructions to Kandimba and returned to the jeep. The men climbed onto the two vehicles which took off at high speed. They crossed the sleeping town and plunged into the bush, on the way to the frontier. Beside the Commander, who was still driving the jeep, was VW. Brave kid! He had not forgotten his pistol or the guard. In the midst of his contradictory feelings, Fearless set to thinking about three generations of fighters represented by him, by the Commissar and by VW. VW's must inevitably be the best, the one that would win the final victory. We are the stones, but merely the stones, of the cathedral. He is the roof, the bell tower . . . Damn, there I go veering off into religion!

'And the Operations Chief? And the guard?' the Commander asked, almost shouting to make himself heard.

'I found him,' VW said. 'The guard stayed with him, I came to inform you. The Operations Chief is waiting for you by the waterfall.

He was quick to say that comrade Commander would arrive with reinforcements, not hang about in Dolisie waiting for news.'

'And what reinforcements! Did you see how they all came forward? They forgot their various tribes, they forgot the inconvenience and danger of the action, they were all volunteers.' He tapped VW on the leg. 'That's why I have confidence in the Angolans. They are muddlers, but they all forget their quarrels and spites to rescue a companion from danger. That is the merit of the Movement, to have achieved this miracle of beginning to transform men. Another generation and the Angolan will be a new man. What is needed is action.'

VW said nothing, he held grimly onto the front of the jeep to withstand the jolts of the vehicle which was careering over ploughed land. But he could not fail to reflect that the Commander seemed to him more hopeful than ever, at a juncture where he might have to start again from scratch with the loss of the best guerrillas.

The jeep raced on, throwing up a screen of dust behind. The lorry had been delayed, by the dust. The high grass at the roadsides lashed the backs of the guerrillas, who had constantly to duck to avoid being hit in the face.

'Okay, comrades?' Fearless asked.

'You could go faster, we can stand it,' said a guerrilla.

Fearless put the accelerator right down. They went on for a few more kilometres and the road became impassable. Day had already broken and the frontier was before them. The frontier was shown by a line of tree-topped mountains. They had to stop the vehicles. They camouflaged them with branches and grass. They formed a column. Fearless said:

'We are going to meet the Operations Chief's group by the waterfall. Once again I say: anyone with cold feet should stay behind!'

'We heard you earlier, comrade Commander. We'd rather get on,' an old guerrilla said.

Fearless went to the head of the column, setting a demon pace. The night of love-making had strongly marked his face. Ondine, oh Ondine, what a woman! He smiled at the recollection. She loves Joao, that is obvious. But she does not want him, so as not to give him further suffering. Her behaviour is not without a certain dignity. Rather, there is a great deal of dignity. However, Joao is her man.

That's what's so silly: acting in the present on the supposition of a doubtful future. One should never act in terms of the future. But who doesn't? Ondine is very human, Fearless decided.

The Stores Chief followed close on the Commander. Weary from sleepless nights, he hid the effort to keep up with the pace set by Fearless. The latter turned back now and then and winked at him. The Stores Chief smiled at seeing the encouragement.

After two hours of marching, they reached the waterfall that marked the frontier. The sun was drowning Mayombe in all shades of green. Am I going to leave this rainbow of greens, Fearless thought in anguish, in exchange for the rainbow of yellows in the centre or the south?

The guerrillas grouped with the Operations Chief came to meet them; among them, New World. They hugged.

'I couldn't do a reconnaissance last night,' Ops said, 'because VW showed up around midnight.'

'And before?'

'We were getting near to Fallen Branch, we saw lots of tracks. It was obvious that the tuga were there. We came this way, since from the frontier it was easier for them to find the path to the Base. The other paths are all mined.'

'So how did the enemy reach the Base?'

'I don't understand,' Ops said. 'Unless there is a path we don't know, which is almost impossible, as the hunters would have said something and we've never found it. That's virtually impossible. Or maybe we were betrayed. Struggle went out after game.'

'Do you still mistrust Struggle?'

'Obviously!'

'Struggle did not betray us.'

'How do you know?'

'I don't know,' Fearless said. 'I feel it. I know the men and I rarely make a mistake about them.'

'So how can it be explained?'

'We'll know later. How many men do you have with you?'

'Nine, comrade Commander.'

'I brought thirty. It is a large enough group to attack the Base, if the enemy are still there.'

'Oh, they never stay long in one of our bases, it's better to drop that.'

'I know. But we must allow for everything. And we don't know the explanation how they got there, so ... We are mystified. Maybe, despite all expectations, they are still there. Soon we'll be believing in ghosts! Let's advance!'

Fearless went to the head of the column. They had to go cross-country, as the enemy might control the access route to the Base. The Operations Chief came to Fearless's side.

'Excuse me, comrade Commander. But you should go in the middle of the column. I shall go at the head.'

'Leave off!'

'No. There might be a mine, one never knows. The commander is too valuable to go at the head.'

Fearless did not answer. He complied. Several guerrillas came between him and the Operations Chief, who was hacking open the scrub with blows of a machete.

They marched all day, as they had to open a path and make detours to avoid the usual route. The creepers protected the secret of their impenetrability, but the men were stubborn and humbled the May-ombe-god at their feet. At six in the afternoon, exhausted, they came to within four hundred metres of the Base.

'We can't go any further,' Fearless said. 'We shall attack at dawn.'

They all agreed. They lay down without eating. There had not been time to think of preparing food, at the moment of departure. It's about twenty-four hours since any of us ate, thought Fearless, and no-one appears to be thinking about that. The Operations Chief's group may have gone without eating for much longer.

Some guerrillas slept as soon as they lay down. No-one had brought blankets to cover himself. The cold of Mayombe crept into their bones, perhaps it would rain, but who cared?

New World came up to Fearless.

'You came quickly.'

'Heavens, it was the least I could do!'

'I never expected that so much strength could be mustered.'

'Nor I. But, as you see, the reality exceeded our expectation. Sometimes we underestimate our militants ...'

'VW should not have come,' New World said. 'He's been marching since yesterday without a break, without sleeping, and, possibly, without eating. And he had to go all night in the forest.'

'You're right. He made an exceptional effort. But he stuck to my side and I forgot what he had already done. He's a brave lad, did very well.'

'Comrade Commander was hard on him . . .'

'Was! But he did very well. That's what I wanted, that at a difficult moment he should be able to do his duty.'

'Do you admit that you were mistaken about him before? That you were unjust?'

'There you go with the same story! Don't annoy me!'

New World did not press it. What kind of man was Fearless? He did not understand him, ran away from his schemes. An adventurer who loves action, he decided next. But the conclusion did not totally satisfy him. There was something missing, something indefinable missing.

'We must talk, comrade Commander. Some other time, more calmly. I think that what separates us is language. We don't speak the same language.'

'I long ago gave up believing in words,' Fearless said. 'But, if you like, why not argue? But now we are too close to Base . . .'

Fearless left him and went to speak to the Operations Chief.

'I can't wait any longer. I am going up to the Base, to try and hear something.'

'It's dangerous, Commander.'

'I shall be careful.'

'I'm going with you then.'

'Let's go.'

They shed their boots and advanced cautiously, avoiding treading on the dry branches that would crack out like shots in the night. I have not had a cigarette yet today, Fearless thought. The smell of a cigarette could carry to the enemy. He chewed a leaf, so that the bitterness would take away his desire to smoke. A laughable gesture, the desire did not come from his mouth, although it was manifest in an excess of saliva.

The Operations Chief went ahead, stalking like a cat. Fearless was burlier, sometimes made imperceptible noises. They had to move at a metre apart from each other, as the night was dark and only the fireflies provided fleeting light. After half an hour, they reached the river. They had covered a hundred metres.

'Let's go upstream,' Fearless suggested, in a whisper.

The other did not reply, but set off on the route. Along the river it was easier to travel, as the ground was clear. But there were stones and one had to feel out the spot with a foot before treading on the ground. They had covered two hundred metres thus, after another half hour.

They stretched out on the ground, side by side, their bodies touching. What lights there might be remained out of sight, as the Base lay at the top of a small bank that led down to the river. They could hear muffled voices in the Base. There were people there. They remained lying down for a good fifteen minutes, relaxing after the incredible effort of moving each muscle imperceptibly to reach there. They could not make out a single word, or identify a familiar voice. Fearless ordered withdrawal.

They retraced the same route, albeit more quickly. Even so, they took half an hour to rejoin the other guerrillas. They lay down at each other's side, without the wish to talk. New World came close, and then the Stores Chief.

'Well then?'

'There are people,' Fearless said. 'But they are speaking softly, cautiously.'

'The tuga must be expecting us to attack,' Ops said. 'So they are observing security precautions. They are always noisy, a tuga camp can be heard a kilometre away, at night.'

'Yes,' New World said, 'they must be expecting us. How close did you get?'

'About a hundred,' Fearless said. 'But from the riverside it is impossible to see anything. Not even a light.'

'Here only the ears matter,' the Stores Chief said.

'We shall wake at five o'clock,' Fearless decided. 'We will need an hour to make our way to where we were. Perhaps longer, as there are many of us.'

'No,' Ops said, 'by day it is easier.'

'But it won't be daylight until six o'clock,' New World said. 'I think the Commander is right.'

New World has settled naturally into the Command, thought Fearless. And it suits him.

'Let's try to sleep,' the Commander said.

But Fearless did not sleep. As soon as he fell into somnolence, he was aroused by anguish. Leli appeared, mixed with Ondine and, above all, Joao. Was he dead or a prisoner? Or lost in the forest? The last hypothesis was the most encouraging, and he held on to it. It was absurd that the Commissar or Muatianvua should make a mistake and run towards the enemy. If VW escaped, why not the rest? Hope built up in him and he was lulled to sleep.

Soon afterwards, the face of Leli came to awaken him, and soak him in cold sweat. Ondine supervened and peace returned to him. A brief respite. Ondine was a link to Joao and soon brought him to mind. The hours did not move forward on his luminous watchface. The green rainbow had disappeared, only the black existed. Black was the colour of his anguish.

I, THE NARRATOR, AM OPERATIONS CHIEF.

I cannot sleep, in this endless night. Fearless, beside me, cannot sleep either. But I can't talk to him. We could never discuss. He is an intellectual, I a peasant's son.

In Dembos, men lived wretchedly in the midst of wealth. Coffee was everywhere, hugging the trees. But they stole from us in the prices, sweat was paid for with a few worthless coins. And the settler plantations spread, and spread, overtaking our small fields on the poorest land.

That is why there was March '61.

I was a child, but I took part in the attack on the settler plantations. I ran forward with stones, among the men with machetes and the rare few who had muskets. We could not look back: the spirit-doctors said that if we did that we would die. The bullets of the whites would be water, they said. After independence those who had fallen in battle would be resurrected. All lies. Today I see it was all lies.

We massacred the settlers, destroyed the plantations, even burned the currency, proclaimed free territory. We were free. For centuries the whites had massacred us, why not massacre them? But war is not waged with hatred alone and the colonial army recovered the territory, the free territory reverted to occupied territory.

I came to the Congo and in the MPLA learned how to wage war, an organized war. I learned to read too. I learned above all that what we did in '61, cutting off the heads of the whites, mesticos, assimilated blacks and Umbundus, was perhaps right for the time. But today no-one can be proud of it. It was a historical inevitability, as the Political Commissar says. I understand the meaning of the words, he is right, in that he is right.

But where he is not right is in standing by the Commander, who is Kikongo. It was the Kikongo who came to mobilize us, who brought the slogans from the Congo to advance haphazardly, without organization. The Kikongo wanted to reconstitute the ancient kingdom of Congo. But they forgot that Dembos and Nambuangongo were always independent of Congo. At least, from a certain stage. That's what the old men in Dembos told me and that's what the MPLA history says. Why the Kingdom of Congo and not Ndongo and Dembos?

When the war was lost in '62, the Kikongo infiltrated MPLA. Not Fearless. He is Kikongo, but was born in Luanda. Fearless is an intellectual, and that makes things more complicated.

He is not asleep.

He cannot sleep. His Base is occupied by the enemy. He was the one who built it, he was the one who forced it on Andre, who wanted it outside. It is his Base. So he suffers. It is a defeat for him. Fearless is an intellectual, an intellectual cannot bear his child to die. We are used to it. Our children died from the bombs, from the machine guns, from the foreman's whip. We are used to seeing our children die. Not he. The Base was his child, he created it against all odds. Against us even, as what we wanted was to return to Dembos and Nambuangongo, where there is really people's war. He believes that struggle is possible here, that it can grow. It is his child, all right, one must understand.

The Commissar says that if we advance the struggle in Cabinda, the other regions will be relieved, as the enemy will have to split his strength. It is true. So I struggle here. But not for Cabinda, which doesn't interest me. I struggle here so that my region should have fewer enemies concentrated there and so should be free.

But Fearless is a man. When he fights, he has the same hatred of the enemy as I do. The reasons are different, but the actions are the same. So I follow him in battle. The bad thing is that he is an intellectual, that's the bad thing: he will never be able to understand the people. His children or brothers did not die in war. No, he cannot understand.

He is not sleeping.

I would like to explain this to him. But I don't know how to put it. And he would not understand.

The luminous dial on Fearless's watch at last showed five o'clock. He tapped the Operations Chief on the shoulder and saw that he was already awake. They went about gently waking the men, who rose immediately.

They divided into two groups, each of about twenty men: one, led by Fearless, would advance by the river to attack the Base; the other, led by the Operations Chief, would make a detour round the Base and take the enemy from behind, when the latter tried to escape through the mountain.

'You must go faster than us,' Fearless said.

The night was still dark. Only at six did the first beams manage to pierce the tree canopy, to restore the green of Mayombe.

The Operations Chief's group moved softly off to the right, to describe a semicircle. The plan would work if there were no-one in the river, thought Fearless. If not, it would be necessary to open fire before taking position for the attack. And a surprise attack was needed to free the prisoners, if there were any.

Fearless kept the best fighters. Even so there were some civilians among them, or guerrillas who had not fought for years. I have the feeling I may have to go into attack alone. Perhaps only New World will keep me company. It would be virtual suicide. Anxiety took hold of him. He would need to spread the men on the small hill alongside the river, climb it without a sound, and only then open fire. I begin to doubt the seriousness of this plan. Improvised. What counts is that we know the terrain perfectly. I don't feel myself, I am over-anxious, my feelings are not under control.

While waiting for the Operations Chief's group to gain ground, Fearless was reflecting.

In Europe I had occasion to play with machines where a little metal ball scores points. All the player has to do is to operate the flippers, when the ball is climbing, or gently direct the ball to the best spot. The delight of the game is not in winning. It is in achieving ecstasy, the oblivion of body and mind in total concentration on the ball which leaps from one side to the other, scoring points. There were moments when I knew I was going to win, reached a state of grace. I so tamed the machine, by the force of my detachment, that my reflexes were in fact perfect: absolute confidence in my fingers that lightly touched the flippers, in my hands that with smooth movements guided the little ball to the desired spot. I reached a state of possession in the machine, it was undoubtedly a sensual pleasure.

In the game, the man who masters himself and at the same time surrenders cannot be a slave. Slaves are such as surrender to the game without mastering themselves or the reverse: it is the dialectic of domination-submission that distinguishes man as master, the dominator, and the slave. Likewise in love.

There are men who win at poker, even when they lose money. They have such control of their nerves, and are at the same time so daring, that their opponents are subjugated, have no initiative, wait for their reactions, their wishes. They are gentlemen who can hazard on a card all that they have won, just for the pleasure of taking the risk. Their opponents may win, in the sense that they walk away with more money than they began with; but the true victor was the one who made them pale, purse their lips, chew their nails, shake, want to piss, and regret for a moment playing. The true master, the conqueror, is not angry at losing: that is his moment of control and, if in fact he imposes his authority, he is content with the defeat. It is men with wretched temperaments who suffer in losing.

In war, likewise, there are masters, those who decide. They are not necessarily chiefs, although these characteristics are only fully revealed in a situation of command. They are the dominant, in the end the most magnanimous to their opponents. They wage war, to some extent like someone playing at roulette: it is a means of confronting oneself with the other face. They are tortured. In clear thinking they understand that the enemy before them, taken as an individual, is a man as they are; but he is defending the side of injustice and must be annihilated. Revolutionary war is much harder in this respect than classical wars. Formerly, the fighter was convinced that the stranger he faced was the sum of all vices, and of all pettiness. It was easy to hate personally the soldier who advanced against him, not the enemy in the abstract, but that very Frank, Schulz, Ahmed or Ngonga who stood before him. Today, what enlightened fighter believes that? All that exists is hatred of the enemy in the abstract, a hatred of the system that individuals are defending. The enemy soldier may even be in contradiction with the cause he is compelled to defend. The revolutionary fighter knows that; he may even take the view that the enemy is a good peasant or a sound worker, useful and combatant in other circumstances, but here poisoned by prejudices, overtrained by the ruling class to kill. The revolutionary must make a compromise between abstract hatred of the enemy and the sympathy the enemy-individual may inspire in him.

So this war is harder, as more humane (yet, more inhumane).

The dominant, the master, would never seek to kill for killing's sake, rather the reverse, would avoid killing. He sees war as a game or love. His moment of loss of clarity is when the abstract hatred becomes concrete in the individual and he advances, frantically lucid, against the soldiers who try to prevent him advancing, they are obstacles that must be brushed from his path. At this moment, the balance is overcome and the physical need – physiologically felt – to carry out the action leads to cold and calculated, implacable hatred. A dominator does not gesticulate in hatred, does not curse; he conserves energy, gestures, hatred; it is his action, rather than symbols, that express his determination.

That is what I should like to be today, but that is a romantic hero. There are comrades dead or at risk of dying and I am unable to master my feelings, I cannot achieve the sensual ecstasy of control, by taking the risk coldly and clearly. There is Joao in the middle, and I cease to be clear. And, more than ever, Leli.

Fearless gave the men the signal to advance. He himself set the

186

example and retraced the route of the night before. The advance was made in a squatting posture, with hands sweeping the ground to avoid a guerrilla stepping on a dry stick. After a while, the thighs and the buttock muscles ached atrociously. But it was the only method. Suppose there were a cobra? That's all we need, he thought. As he already knew the way, they reached the river in twenty minutes. Fearless rested, before going on.

New World came and whispered:

'Now it's better I go in front.'

'No, I'm going,' Fearless said. 'Come behind me.'

They lowered weapons to a firing position and resumed the march. They stopped at the last bend in the river.

'Now we must wait for dawn before advancing. We will not be able to position the comrades properly.'

He was closer to the Base than on the previous night. The guerrillas silently sat. Our progress was perfect, Fearless thought. Only a guerrilla forewarned would have spotted our march. When will I be able to smoke?

At ten to six, the trees began to take on vague shape. Five minutes later the outline of the trunks could be made out. Mayombe was being reborn from the darkness. Fearless stood up and hissed to the men:

'One on each side of the river, at ten metre intervals.'

Fearless saw New World place himself at the first point, across the stream. He is brave, he will be a good man in charge of Dolisie. Life is teaching him to be more relative.

Progress was still more slow, as they had to crawl over the rocks. Sometimes they had to go into fairly deep water. The water was cold and their wet clothing stuck chill to the body. Mayombe had already regained its green rainbow. Fearless took it as a first sign of welcome.

They were just turning the last bend. It would be sufficient to advance another twenty metres and the fan formation would be made naturally. Fearless and New World completed the bend. They stiffened suddenly. Fifteen metres from them was a light-skinned man, washing himself in the river. A mulatto, Fearless thought. The man had his back to them. The half light still did not allow much to be made out clearly. The Commander and New World exchanged questioning looks.

The plan has failed, Fearless thought. They needed to advance to where the soldier was, because only from there could they cut off the enemy's flight by the other river bank, and make him climb the mountain, where the other group were waiting. Moreover, if they climbed the bank from the spot where they were, they would not surge into the middle of the Base. They would have to advance twenty metres over open ground. They would not have the advantage of surprise and would be an easy target.

Wait they could not: if one tuga was washing, others would soon follow. Leli reappeared and Fearless made a sign to New World to keep moving.

They advanced even more slowly, with AKs at firing position. It was a mestico, there was no doubt. He undressed completely and plunged into the water. Still with his back turned. Fearless advanced more quickly than New World, he was in better training. Five metres' distance. The soldier was covered in soap. If I could reach him and knife him, everything would be saved. He could not go any nearer, he would be noticed. Fearless indicated a halt and signalled to the guerrillas to climb the slope. They would be bound to make a noise. When the soldier turned around, he would kill him. Then he would run, on his own, to lead the attack and to block the enemy's exit. It was the only solution.

The men on the left bank of the stream crossed over and joined the others. Only six comrades could be seen. The others were hidden by the bend in the river. It's few for the attack, the Commander thought. Maybe the example will be infectious and they will advance. With civilians one never knows! What's more the civilians were further back, in the most difficult position to move into attack.

The guerrillas had begun to crawl up the slope. They made some slight noise, as was inevitable. Fearless had eyes only for the mestico, who would now see everything. The latter emerged from the water, cleaning his ears. It's now, the Commander thought. The mulatto heard the sound of a pebble rolling down the hillside and turned. Fearless gripped the AK.

The man saw the guerrillas, saw Fearless's AK aimed at him and remained indifferent, with his legs apart in the middle of the river that came up to his knees. His arms were stretched slowly out from his body, until he held a crucifixion pose. Fearless recognized that it was Theory.

The Commander lowered the weapon and revealed himself. A few seconds' hesitation. Then Fearless clearly saw Theory's heart beginning to beat somewhere around his stomach. The guerrillas were nearing the top of the bank. Soon they would be in position and waiting for a burst from the Commander as a signal to open fire. Fearless went up to Theory.

'What's going on?' he whispered.

'Nothing,' the teacher replied, in a similar tone.

'The tuga?'

'What tuga?'

'Wasn't the Base attacked?'

'No.'

The Commander, incredulous but relieved without understanding anything, turned to his men.

'Stop, comrades. Stop. It's our people in the Base after all.'

The guerrillas looked down and saw Theory. The order was passed to all the guerrillas.

'Theory, go and warn the Base that it is us who are coming in. If not, someone may still open fire. New World, run and warn Ops.'

The assurance that the Base was still intact began gradually to invade all of them. They heard Theory shout, then went forward calmly, but still in formation. Guerrillas came out of the huts, with weapons in their hands. They saw the others who were advancing on them, with weapons in their hands. In the middle, a mulatto, totally naked, who was shouting:

'Our chaps have arrived. Fearless has arrived. Don't shoot, don't shoot! Fearless has arrived.'

After the initial surprise, the guerrillas ran towards each other. They hugged one another warmly. Those who remained at the Base were a mere dozen, with the arrival of reinforcements they felt that danger was already remote. Those who were arriving laughed at the relief of finding them alive. The confusion of shouts and laughter was tumultuous. The men looked at each other, pinched themselves at seeing companions before them, and hugged one another.

Fearless left the Commissar for the last. He almost ran to him, with open arms, and the AK was forgotten against a tree. His nerves were giving, he wanted to hug Joao, to laugh and cry. But the Commissar saw the gesture and stretched out a cold hand. Fearless halted, hesitated, pulled a face. He shook the hand softly. He rushed to his camp-bed and lay down on it.

He lit a first cigarette and consumed it ravenously.

◆

The seniors were meeting in the Command hut. Fearless was smoking constantly, and staring at the roof.

'What happened then?' the Operations Chief asked.

The Commissar sat on a camp-bed. He lit a cigarette. He already has his own cigarettes, Fearless noted. Although staring at the roof, he was conscious of the gestures of the other man, who avoided looking at him.

'Theory went to the river,' the Commissar said, addressing the Operations Chief, but speaking for Fearless. 'We were on stand-by, had dug trenches, had sent you to control the road. (The Commissar's voice was steady, aggressively steady, as the Commander noticed.) Suddenly, in the river Theory saw a snake coming. It looked as if it was going to attack him. Theory gave it a burst and then another to follow. Hearing that, I ordered everyone into the trenches. Then, Theory came to explain what had happened. We noticed the absence of VW and of the comrade who was on guard. We were so few, we were left with still smaller manpower.'

The guerrillas who had just arrived listened in stupefaction to the story related by the Commissar.

'So it was a snake then?' asked one. 'A snake who invaded the Base?'

'So I ruined everything,' VW said, dejectedly. 'But I heard a shout "take him alive" . . .'

'I was the one who shouted "take to the trenches",' the Commissar said.

'Comrade Commissar shouted "take to the trenches" and I heard "take them alive"?' VW reiterated. 'I ruined everything . . .'

The guerrillas were beginning to come out of their state of stupor when they heard, coming from the Commander's camp-bed, a kind of deep roar, emerging from the stomach, which was soon released into the most monumental burst of laughter in the entire history of the Base. The burst of laughter made the men quiver, climbed above the tree trunks and rose to merge with the wind that shook the leaves of Mayombe.

'Comrade Commander laughs?' the Commissar asked. 'I don't see the joke! All the efforts made were useless, do you understand? Do you understand? You brought so many people, dragged them from bed, paralysed all the Movement's work in Dolisie, and yet you laugh? All for the sake of a cowardly kid, who couldn't stand up to a few bursts of gunfire. And the comrade laughs?'

The Commissar was in front of the Commander, with his legs apart and a shaking finger pointing at him.

'The invasion of the snake!' Fearless said, in the midst of choking laughter.

Some of the guerrillas were smiling. VW shrank into a corner, fascinated by the Commander. Theory, still scantily dressed, shrank back likewise. New World put on a stern look, as he eyed Fearless.

Suddenly, Fearless sprang from the bed.

'What would you have us do? Now, all that's left for us is to laugh. If anyone doesn't understand, patience, let him not understand! But I would rather it had been a snake than the tuga invading the Base. Useless effort? They think it useless? We mobilized more than thirty men in under an hour, with civilians among them. Do they know what that means? If they don't know, then I don't understand why they are here claiming to struggle. It was the most extraordinary example of collective solidarity I've seen. And of fighting spirit. For me it's enough. I am happy to find you all alive. And I find the story a joke, I do find it so, yes. And then? And then?'

He went back to lying down. Theory noticed the tears that made the Commander's eyes flash.

'It was my fault,' he said. 'I should never have fired, when the enemy was expected. I should be punished.'

'It was my fault,' VW said, standing up and turning to the Commander. 'The guard said it sounded like bursts from a Pepesha, that it was better to wait. But I told him that I heard a shout of "take them alive" and I dragged him out. It was my fault.'

'The comrades will be tried later,' the Commissar said.

'But why didn't you inform Dolisie, comrade Commissar?' New World asked. 'When you realized that the comrades had taken flight, you should have thought they would go and inform Dolisie. Why didn't you send someone immediately? It was obvious that comrade Commander would come racing here . . .'

'We expected that VW and the other would show up by six in the evening. They might have retreated a short way and, hearing nothing further, would return. Then it was night-time. I preferred not to send anyone. Two would have to go and the strength would have been down too low!'

'Yes,' Fearless said, 'the Commissar did right.'

A silence came. The Commissar himself looked in puzzlement at the Commander who had come to his rescue. The latter was smoking, still staring at the roof. The cigarette shook in his hand.

'Comrade Theory must be punished,' Fearless went on. 'As for VW . . . Comrades must see that it is not his fault. The fault is of the person who sent him here without preparation. He is not able, nor could be able, to distinguish our weapons from the enemy's. He has never fought, is short on coolness. Even so, he had the courage to go and recover his pistol and to fetch the guard. Few of you would have done it, in his situation. Let's be objective!'

'That is a matter for the Command to decide,' the Commissar interrupted.

'Effectively! But as we are discussing here, I have already given my view.'

'Why not have a public hearing, a meeting of all the comrades who are here now?' New World suggested. 'It is much more democratic!'

'That is not according to the Movement's statutes,' the Commissar said.

'Agreed, comrade Commissar. But comrade Commander has spoken and spoken well about the extraordinary effort that was made. This affair has touched so many people that perhaps it would be a

192

good idea, to extend the mobilization it has given rise to, if we carried on discussion in a meeting, where everyone could express his opinion. Like that, this whole affair might be very positive in politicizing and mobilizing comrades.'

'I agree,' Fearless said.

'Me too,' Ops said.

New World has guessed that he is being thought about for promotion and is already taking on his role, Fearless thought, or is he naturally taking a lead as an enlightened cadre?

'I bow to the will of the majority in the Command,' the Commissar said gloomily.

Until lunch-time, nothing more was said and the ones who had come from Dolisie slept. After lunch, there was a general meeting.

By the vote of the great majority of the guerrillas, VW went unpunished. Theory had the extenuating circumstances of declaring that the snake was going to attack. He was punished with extra guard duties for a month.

At night, Fearless sensed that the Commissar was twisting in bed, but in the end he himself fell asleep, overcome by two sleepless nights.

On the following morning, there was a meeting of the Command. It was decided to attack Fallen Branch to force the enemy to withdraw from the camp. That camp was a sword hanging over the guerrilla Base. It had to go. Fearless would return to Dolisie to take up his post and prepare logistics for the operation. Meanwhile, the civilians should make their way back to Dolisie and try to send more guerrillas into the area.

Fearless and the Commissar bade each other good-bye with a cold handshake.

I, THE NARRATOR, AM OPERATIONS CHIEF.

Once more Fearless has proved to be a great commander. Another blow at the Commissar's pride, as he was already taking himself for greater. This Commissar is a child, wants to pit himself haphazardly against the Commander, and ends up looking ridiculous.

The guerrillas understood and admired Fearless. In the meeting, the guerrillas praised the Commander for the speed with which he acted and for the courage he breathed into the very civilians. Deserved praise. I joined in it myself. He is like that: when he has to defend a comrade, he drops everything and rushes forward.

And that outburst of laughter? The Commissar did not understand, but the guerrillas who came in the reinforcement understood and supported it. Isn't it really a laugh that a snake had provoked all this? Obviously the Commissar did not like it, he was to blame for what happened, when he was unable to make a quick decision. But the incident led to a great mobilization and Fearless was able to take advantage of it and to support it. He spoke in such a way that they all felt they had behaved like heroes. Who does not like to be regarded as a hero?

Today, Fearless won the support of the guerrillas at the Base and those from Dolisie. Nothing else is talked about, all the talk is about the Commander.

They have forgotten that he is Kikongo, just see that he is a great commander.

If they all think like that, especially the Stores Chief, who is already an elder, then perhaps it is true. I begin to think we were unfair to him.

He is an intellectual. The people understand him only when he expresses himself in action. And what a way he expressed himself!

CHAPTER 5

The Mulberry Tree

Fearless returned to Dolisie, accompanied by the civilians. The guerrillas who had come as reinforcements agreed to stay on a while longer at the base, to take part in the attack. It was agreed that their things should be sent to the interior immediately: blanket, cartridge-belt, etc. The Commander was amazed at the enthusiasm of the fighters. The Stores Chief wanted to remain, but Fearless insisted on his returning with him to Dolisie.

On the way, Fearless felt a delight that he was going to meet Ondine again. He soon restrained it. He thought of the Commissar and his hostility. That would pass! He regretted only that he had to remain in Dolisie and could not take part in the operation. Would the Commissar be capable of leading it? It was a long time since they had mounted so important an action and it had always been he, Fearless, who had led them. Joao could still do foolish things. There I am thinking of him as a child! The metamorphoses are speedy and we go on seeing others in their old skin. He is forging himself a Commander's cuirass, a cuirass full of sharp spikes, and I am still seeing him as a butterfly pupa.

When they reached town, Fearless at once found the letter with the leadership's instruction: New World was put in charge of Dolisie provisionally; Fearless was to resume his duties as Commander immediately, owing to the imminent danger of a colonialist attack; he was to prepare himself for transfer to the East. Fearless ran out of the office, and went to show the message to Ondine.

'Are you happy about this?'

'Oh, yes, everything meets my wishes. I can take part in the attack and, later, I start for the Eastern Front, to open a new Region. But don't tell anyone that, these are military secrets.'

'Then you shouldn't have told me . . .'

'It's my perpetual liberalism, as New World would say!'

'We shall meet again in the East,' she said.

Fearless gave her an anxious look.

'I don't think so. The East is big and I am going to the interior a lot. Anyway, I haven't seen anything about you yet. No, we shan't meet.'

'Why?'

She stared at him in mute invitation. Fearless went out, without a word, controlling his desire.

He immediately sent a comrade to the Base, to summon New World. And he rushed about town, choosing the few guerrillas who remained, preparing the mortars and the other weapons, buying tinned food for the mission. He did not dine.

He returned to the house at eleven at night. When he entered his room, Ondine was lying in the bed, awake.

'What are you doing here?'

'I was waiting for you.'

'Go to your room.'

'Why?'

'I left the Base this morning, did eight hours' march on foot, then did not have a moment's pause in getting things ready. I am beat, need sleep. Heavens! That's not the reason. Go to your room.'

'I'll just stay and watch you sleep.'

'Go to your room.'

She went out crossly. Fearless, still dressed, threw himself down where her body had left a mark, and felt her warmth. The warmth that came from the bed poured into him, and he felt violent desire. He smoked to quell this desire. The weariness of the journey and of intensive work finally overcame him.

But Ondine came into his dream, offering her naked self to him and saying: 'I love Joao.' Fearless would wake up, smoke, fall asleep again. Ondine was now running over the savanna of Huila, her hair was long and black, Leli's hair, her arms were outstretched to him. But he was a hundred metres below, at the foot of the precipice, and Ondine-Leli was throwing herself into the void to fall into his arms. An interminable night. He rose with the sun's rays, with swollen eyes and a headache.

Late in the afternoon New World arrived. They prepared the mission together: they had assembled twenty more guerrillas; their strength would be fifty. Young boys had volunteered and three were

196

accepted to keep the mortars in ammunition. They had mobilized all the fit men, women and children, to carry food and the mortars as far as the Base. Departure was set for the following morning.

Fearless put New World in the picture on urgent matters, then went to introduce him at Stores as the new man in charge. They went to dinner at ten o'clock. When they were seated at table, New World said:

'I don't have any experience of this. I don't know why they appointed me . . .'

'I supported your candidacy for this post.'

'You?'

'Does it surprise you?'

'A little, yes. It seems we don't share the same ideas. Or is it only the words?'

Fearless took a draught of beer. Ondine was the third person at dinner, but was not paying attention to what they were saying.

'We don't share the same ideas,' Fearless said. 'You are the machine type, one of those who is going to set up the unique, all-powerful Party in Angola. I am the type who could never belong to the machine. I am the type whose historic role ends when we have won the war. But my aim is the same as yours. I know that to achieve my aim, an intermediate phase is needed. Types like you will fill this intermediate phase. So, I think I did right in supporting your name. One day, in Angola, there will no longer be any need for rigid machines, and that is my aim. But I shall not achieve it.'

'Meanwhile what are you doing?'

'I am waging war. Through my military action, I allow the machine to be installed.'

'And when the machine is installed, what will you do?'

'I don't know. I never had an answer to that question. What I do know, what I want you to understand, is that the revolution we are making is half the revolution I want. But it is the possible, I know my limits and the country's limits. My role is to contribute to this half-revolution. So I go to the end, in the knowledge that in relation to the ideal I have set myself, my action is half useless, or rather only half useful.'

'Basically, that is my position,' New World said. 'I know that

197

communism will not be achieved, in my lifetime, that the most we can manage is to reach socialism. It will require many years to overcome capitalist relations of production and the mentality they leave behind. It's the same position!'

'No, it is not. You are in the struggle for independence, and at the same time preparing for socialism. Your motive is political. For you, everything occurs in terms of the political objective to be attained.'

'And you?'

'I? I am, in your terminology, adventurist. I should like the discipline of war to be established in terms of man and not the political objective. My guerrillas are not a group of men deployed to destroy the enemy, but a gathering of different, individual beings, each with his subjective reasons to struggle and who, moreover, behave as such.'

'I don't understand you.'

'You can't understand me. Nor can I explain, everything is still so muddled. For example, I am happy when I see a young man decide to build himself a personality, even if politically that signifies individualism. But he is a new man beginning to be born, despite everyone and everything, a man free of pettiness and prejudice, and I am satisfied. Even if to do it he infringes generally accepted discipline and morality. That's an example, at least ... I know only that your position is fairer, since it conforms more closely to the current situation. You use men, at this stage it is necessary. I cannot manipulate men, I respect them too much as individuals. For that reason, I cannot belong to a machine. It is my fault. Fault! It is no-one's fault.'

'You are demoralized, Fearless.'

'No,' he said, with a glance at Ondine. 'I am anguished, because I struggle between reason and sentiment.'

She heard and lowered her eyes. New World was too busy analysing what Fearless had said.

Dinner ended and they went to their respective rooms.

A little after he had laid down, Fearless heard old Kandimba calling him from outside. Dressed only in trousers, he went to see. The old man said:

'There's a comrade who wants to talk to the boss. As the other man is still new, I came to call comrade Commander.'

198

'All right. Who is it?'

'He's there outside.'

Fearless, with an inward groan, went to the veranda. He looked at the newcomer and, although the face was not strange to him, he could not quite place him. The man came forward, with a smile.

'What luck! It's the same gentleman Commander whom I met. You recognize me, don't you?'

'I don't see . . .'

'From the time you caught the workers who were chopping the trees . . .'

'I know!' Fearless shouted. 'You're the mechanic. What are you doing here?'

'I came to talk to you. I want to work for the Movement. I left the village yesterday morning, reached the Congo without difficulty. I came to report.'

The Commander remained hesitant for a moment, then on impulse hugged him.

'You are welcome, comrade. What made you decide?'

'Well, that discussion the comrades had with us began to convince me. Truly we are exploited and must struggle. But what really convinced me was when the comrades risked so much to return the money to me. Then, yes, I understood it all. The comrades were really defending the people. I began to listen to the radio, "Angola Combatente". I learned some things there. Then I talked to my friends, we began to discuss the situation and MPLA. We thought we could work for the Movement right there, without anyone knowing. But the comrades did not show up again there. So I came here to make contact.'

'Do you want to return to the village?'

'I could go there, if the comrades think it useful, to make contact with the others. But I would rather be a guerrilla. But I don't even know how to use a weapon . . .'

'That can be learned.'

'There are others who want to come, and the rest who want to stay there and help the comrades.'

'That is very important too. Comrades who stay in the villages, to provide us with information and to help in whatever way is needed.'

199

'The army and PIDE took a lot prisoners, they said that the people had helped the comrades. They were wild because they had many soldiers killed. But the people were more rebellious. The people are beginning to understand who after all is a bandit!'

'Let us talk later. Have you eaten already?'

'No, nothing.'

'Kandimba, find some food for this comrade, please.'

'At this time?'

'At this very time. The comrade has travelled a long way and has not eaten. Hunger does not have a time-table.'

'There's only bread and tea.'

'That's a start,' the mechanic said.

'So come and eat,' Fearless said.

He kept the mechanic company, chatting, while the latter ate. Then he showed him a place to sleep.

'Tomorrow morning speak to comrade New World, who is in charge here. Anyway, you know him already.'

With a smile, he went to lie down. The Commissar had done good work, when he went to return the money.

Fearless made an effort to sleep, but he did not succeed. Ondine would come to rouse him from somnolence. He imagined her body stirring in bed, recalled the minutest details of her body, her warmth.

He went out of his room and opened her door.

'I was expecting you,' she said.

Fearless ran to the arms she opened for him.

'Why do you run away from me?' she asked.

Fearless took his lips from the breast that had interrupted conversation and said:

'You love Joao. One day you will find Joao again.'

'At this instant I love you. It is you I love.'

'No. You desire me, that is different. But you love Joao. That is love. Keeping a tenderness for the same man, even if you desire others at various moments.'

She caressed his head.

'We could stay together. We would be happy. Each with our temporary escapades, but always returning to the other.'

'No, I could not stand it. Joao, yes. With Joao, you could do that.

He would adjust, is a different man. I belong to a past generation, that which was scarred by the total morality of a traditionalist and Christian society.'

They made love. Desperately. Fearless knew that it would be the last time: after the mission, he would return to Dolisie only when he received a marching order for the East. Meanwhile, Ondine would already have left.

They lit cigarettes. She cradled him over her breasts.

'I love you, Fearless. I love you and, at the same time, you scare me because you are too much master of yourself.'

'If I were master of myself, I should not have come here tonight. It is a sign of weakness. Basically, I am weak.'

'You are a man, that's all.'

Fearless exhaled. He studied the whirls of smoke.

'I always wanted to overcome my human side. To be God or a legendary hero. You bring confusion between Joao and me. What you love in men is what there is in common between Joao and myself. Only, you don't know him well enough to realize that it is the common feature. It is as if we were the same person, but with ten years of the revolution in the interval, do you understand? He belongs to the generation that has won, and by overcoming himself he will be able to understand and accept you. I understand you, but I don't accept you as you are. I would try to change you in my image. I would destroy you, tame you. I cannot do it.'

'And suppose I wished it?'

'What for? To hate me after two years? I have an image of myself: a snail with his house on his back. Like that I feel free, myself. Love, desire, or passion could make me give up this image. But I should lose my self-respect. It is as if I were wounded and felt afraid of dying.'

'Are you afraid of dying'

'No, I don't think so. But it would be dreadful if, when I were dying, I should be afraid of death. I should lose my self-respect. The persona I had made for myself would be destroyed in a second and I should die with the feeling of having been an imposter. It would be dreadful! That is why I face up to death. I am not afraid of death. I am afraid of feeling fear, fear of dying. That is why I am always running risks, to face me with myself.'

201

'It's stupid!' she said.

'It is not. Nothing about a man is stupid. There is always a reason, which may be psychological, for every attitude. It would be stupid, if it were gratuitous. In me it is not gratuitous, since it is an intimate need. Obviously, if I said this to New World, he would think it was gratuitous. But New World is a politician. That's what I wanted to explain to him, but he cannot understand. He is a button on the machine, a cog, nothing more. I am, as you say, a man. Above all, a tortured man, a loner. That's why I feel I fit Mayombe, where we are all loners.'

'I desire you,' she said.

They made love. Interminably. Let this night not end, he wished. But at four in the morning they must leave. New World was taking care of everything so that he could rest. He looked at the luminous dial: one in the morning.

'We have three hours,' said he.

'We have our whole life,' said she.

'No.'

She embraced him.

'I am going to win you in such a way that you will run to me as soon as you have destroyed Fallen Branch. I have three hours in which to do it.'

'Don't have any illusions. I shall not come to you. See and feel this night as the last. It's for the best.'

'No,' she shouted. 'I don't want it to be the last. It is as if you were dead to me.'

'Joao is your man, get that right into your head.'

'For him I feel tenderness.'

'More than that. Love. The need for him, for his presence, will come with time. And the image you have of me will vanish, when you realize that what you love in me is Joao.'

They made love anew. They lit up cigarettes.

'May I know where you are going?' she asked.

'I don't know. But I suspect the target will be the Chela Mountain in Huila. Or Huambo.'

'I shall ask to be assigned there. They must need teachers.'

'I shall object. And I am one of the people in charge.'

'Why are you cruel?'

'I am sensible. I am concerned for your good. It is to your good that you meet Joao again, a different Joao, whom I have already glimpsed but whom you do not know. A Joao who is relativist and human, without the straitjacket of narrow ideology.'

They made love wordlessly. At four o'clock, Fearless left the bed.

'Will you come back?' she asked.

'No.'

And he left the room to go and equip himself. She did not abandon the bed, as she enjoyed the warmth and the smell he had left.

◆

The long convoy of guerrillas, women and children reached the Base at midday.

Fearless noted that the Commissar was unhappy at seeing him. He had wanted to lead the attack on his own, it would have been his affirmation. The presence of the Commander placed him in a subordinate role.

'Let's go to the river, we must talk,' Fearless said.

With ill grace, the Commissar picked up his weapon and followed him to the river. Fearless sat on the usual trunk.

'I am going to be transferred to the Eastern Front, possibly to Huila. It is to open a new Region. You will replace me here. It is possible that this will be my last operation in Cabinda. I came, because it was my duty. But you will command the attack. I shall form part of the Command, but you will be Commander.'

'Why?'

'Because you can do it and must gain experience. In effect, we are changing places. Agreed?'

'If that's how you want it,' the Commissar said.

They looked at each other in silence. Fearless tried to sustain a natural manner, the Commissar blazed hostility.

'It's useless for us to behave like two fighting cocks,' Fearless said.

The other shrugged.

'Whatever you wish!' Fearless said.

And he returned to the Base, an AK perched on his strong shoulder, followed by the Commissar, thin but muscular.

The Command drew up a plan of attack, based on two mortars and bazookas, followed by an assault group. Fallen Branch was situated beside an accessible hill, on which the mortars could be set up. The assault group would remain in the only spot open for an enemy flight, namely exactly opposite the hill for the mortars. The five bazookas would remain at the side, to destroy the trenches the tuga had made. The object of the operation was to eliminate the enemy, to force them to abandon Fallen Branch. The tuga were in company strength.

'We can annihilate them,' Fearless said.

'Suppose the mortars fell on us?' the Commissar asked.

'Impossible,' said Muata, head of the mortar battery. 'We shall be very close and from the hill the camp is easy to see. It is impossible for a single shell to go astray. They will all fall bang in the middle of the camp.'

'The mortars will give the signal and then the bazookas will operate,' Fearless said. 'Meanwhile, the assault group advances.'

'Assignments?' the Operations Chief asked.

'Muata will command the artillery, ten men. You will command the bazooka group, eleven men, five bazooka-men, five loaders and you. The Commissar will command the assault group, thirty men.'

'And comrade Commander?'

'I shall be in the assault group, but the Commissar will lead.'

They left next day. Some of the civilians helped carry the mortars, the rest returned to Dolisie. Three boys also went along, to feed the mortars with ammunition. The boys need to be in touch with the war, Fearless had said.

The attack would be at dawn.

I, THE NARRATOR, AM STRUGGLE.

Tomorrow we are going to advance to Fallen Branch. A dangerous mission, because it is them or us. Fallen Branch occupied by the enemy is another knife in the people of Cabinda. And where are these people?

204

They allow themselves to be dominated, don't support us. Is it their fault? No, it is the fault of whoever has been unable to convince them.

Tomorrow, in the attack, how many natives of Cabinda will there be? One, I myself. One, among fifty. How to convince the guerrillas from the other areas that my people are not just made up of traitors? How to convince them that I am myself not a traitor?

Half-whispered words, conversations broken off when I appear, all that shows they suspect me. Only the Commander is not suspicious.

We joined the guerrilla war in the same year. I was the guide, he was the teacher at Base. They did not want him to fight, they gave him the war communiques to draft. Until one day he demanded that they let him fight. He never again wrote war communiques, he began to live them.

We have always been together, he knows that I would not betray. But how many think as he does? He's going away, it's said that he is going away to the East. Who will defend me from the others, who will have the courage to oppose tribalism?

I shall have to be the one to assert myself, by being braver than anyone. And Nzambi knows how afraid I am! But what will become of my people if the only man from Cabinda behaves badly?

Sometimes I think the others were right, that it was necessary to eliminate the Cabindas. That's at moments of anger. But wouldn't my brother, properly mobilized, be able to struggle? Yes, he would, all it needs is for the struggle to advance.

On the day after tomorrow, in battle, I shall be like Fearless. My people require it.

Progress to Fallen Branch went normally. Sometimes they spotted new trails, opened up by the enemy in search of the Base. The reconnaissance patrols came and went, minutely studying the ground. Any premature alarm would destroy the surprise element. The bulk of the column advanced in short stages, of an hour's march.

At three in the afternoon they were five hundred metres from the camp. Voices, shouts and laughter could be heard. The artillery group moved away, to climb the mountain where they would pass the night. Firing would begin at six in the morning precisely.

The guerrillas relaxed in silence. Those in charge whispered, as they agreed the final details. They ate at five. At this point, the group of bazooka-men, under the Operations Chief, broke away. They would take up position at night, before sleeping, and at ten to six would proceed to the camp. The assault group would stay on the spot, and begin the advance at half past five in the morning. They were too numerous a group to sleep close to the enemy: there is the uncontrollable cough or the nightmare that makes someone cry out.

Fearless drew close to Theory.

'How is it?'

'Normal,' Theory said.

'Nerves?'

'Great!'

They fell silent. Fearless was smoking, hiding the flame of his cigarette in a cupped hand.

'Is the Commissar annoyed with you?' Theory asked.

'Yes.'

'He came back from Dolisie changed. Headstrong, full of authority. One can see that it is still a bit forced, but it suits him.'

'He will make a good Commander.'

'It's a pity you're going away. You'll be missed here. Now that there's a chance of growth . . .'

'There too, so it seems. I like Mayombe, but I'd very much like to reach the highlands as well.'

'Me too. But you will be missed here. I don't know if the Commissar will put up with the men.'

'He will, yes. Better than I. And I don't know if you have already noted an easing of relations.'

'Yes, since Andre's exit.'

'The mechanic we captured is in Dolisie. He came to join the Movement. The war is advancing.'

They lay down. The Commissar made no approach, nor did Fearless. The Commander once again began a sleepless night. Ondine. Ondine was trying to grasp him, drawing him towards the warmth of her bosom and he was struggling. Yield once more and he would be captive. Ondine tamed men and he, at heart, felt weak against her. Only Joao, a tempered Joao, would have the strength to escape being dominated. He was beginning to age, to share pleasure, solitude

206

weighed on him. If he returned to Dolisie, he would be trapped in her web. He felt that as he bade her farewell. His 'no' had come from him as a sigh of relief. On the march he was a free man. Now came the ghosts, the visions, but it did not matter. During the day he was free, himself, a baobab in the midst of savanna. Tomorrow would be the battle, his supreme moment of fear and, afterwards, when the firing began, liberation.

He turned to Theory. The latter was not yet asleep. Fearless whispered to him:

'What matters is action. The problems of the Movement settle themselves, through armed action. The mobilization of the Cabinda people comes through developing action. Personal problems are settled in action. Not haphazard action, action for its own sake. But revolutionary action. What is important is to make the Revolution, even if it is going to be betrayed.'

Theory did not reply. They went back to trying to sleep. Theory with his fear, the Commander with his ghosts.

They rose at a quarter past five. The Commissar came up.

'Comrade Commander, wouldn't it be better to divide into two groups? One led by me and the other by you? But they should keep close to each other. It is easier.'

'Agreed. But you are the one to give orders.'

'All right.'

They crept forward like cats. The packs had remained at the rear position, where they had slept. The progress reminded Fearless of the dawn march to attack the Base. Very different. Now he was advancing, in the certainty of the enemy presence, but alone with his ghosts. The other time there had been Joao's life at the centre, the anguish that gripped his belly and rose to his chest, whence it had radiated all his body.

They reached fifty metres from the camp. The two groups divided, completely cutting off enemy flight. If the mortars and bazookas did their task well, the tuga would run away. They could do this on the left only, where the Commissar's group were. As soon as the shells began to fall, the two groups would advance further to prepare the assault. The plan could not fail, the enemy would lose a company in battle. Above all, the people would know and would say that the Movement was really strong. That was fundamental.

It was five minutes before firing was due to start. Fearless lay down, rubbing his face against a creeper. He was thinking of Ondine: Leli had remained in the darkness, only Ondine appeared. Ondine and her tenderness hidden beneath a cloak of coldness: it was a pretence; but he tore off the cloak, the pretence was destroyed and Ondine came, naked, an ocean of tenderness in her eyes, a volcano in her thighs. Ondine, Ondine, why did we meet so late? It was irremediably late. Five years ago perhaps it would have been possible.

Two minutes to go. Then one. The men eyed their watches. Fearless observed them. In his group were Truth, calm as always; Theory, nervously chewing a piece of grass; Muatianvua, looking at him, in expectation of orders; Pangu-Akitina, who smiled at him. Then there was no time to wait, just Ondine in the middle, as the hour had come.

The first shells made the Mayombe-god shake. The monkeys leapt from tree to tree, gibbering. Muata was efficient, the shells rained down at a devilish rate, slap in the middle of the camp. The tuga were shouting, moaning, cursing. Then Fearless heard the first round of bazooka fire.

It was Miracle, the best. The first enemy group to realize what was happening rushed into a trench. Miracle stood up, went forward two steps and fired a missile that annihilated the enemy before they could properly burrow into the trench. Those who were running for a second trench remained stupefied, frozen, at seeing Miracle, on foot, bare-chested, and loading the bazooka. But it was another guerrilla who placed a second missile in the midst of the enemy. There was yet a third group who tried to move to the trenches, but the Operations Chief's AK and the Pepeshas sang out loud and Miracle put the finishing touch, again.

Mortars continued to fall. The officers had lost control of the men. All that remained was flight.

Fearless followed the battle by ear. It was still too soon to act. Moreover it was for the Commissar to give orders, as he was right in front of the enemy's escape route. He, Fearless, could see nothing from there.

At that moment he noticed a slim figure who leapt into the air and tumbled back into a crouch. It was Joao. What is he doing? Advancing on the enemy? Madness, Fearless thought. The Commissar raised his head and they looked at each other. They were twenty metres from each other. Fearless gave him an imperative signal to stop. Joao shrugged his shoulders and did another somersault, which took him out of sight.

The first soldiers were rushing to that side. Fearless's group opened fire and they dropped down an embankment, sheltered from the fire.

So, Fearless viewed the scene. As if in a film. Joao became aware of the embankment and advanced so as to remain in front of the enemy, when the latter went into the valley. But he had not given any order to his men to advance. He had done so alone, as a challenge to Fearless's courage: it was a duel that he was forcing on the Commander, a kind of Russian roulette. Madness, Fearless thought. The enemy were bound to advance that way, forty or fifty men would advance by the embankment, protected from fire by Fearless's group. Before them they would find the Commissar, with an AK.

It was a film. Struggle, who was in the Commissar's group, also realized what was happening. He jumped from his position, and ran to the Commissar. There would be two weapons at least to hold off the enemy counterattack. But his run was brusquely interrupted, his head was thrown violently back by a machine gun burst from a Breda. Struggle died instantaneously.

The enemy were now sending fierce fire against the position of the Commissar, who was shielded by a tree-trunk. The Breda swept the open space between Joao and his men, who did not dare leave their shelters. Fearless picked out the Commissar's AK, recognized its rhythm: a three-round burst, a silence, a two-round burst, a silence. Soon it would be all over as an enemy bazooka would destroy Joao's precarious refuge.

It was a film. And he a spectator. With a feeling of impotence.

And then, as always, the itch began in Fearless's belly. As he leapt from cover, he shouted: 'MPLA advance!' Hurling a first grenade down the embankment, he ran forward. Theory followed him immediately. Truth likewise. Muatianvua likewise. Following on came the rest. Fearless's plan was to switch to a grenade attack on the embankment, to sow confusion among the enemy and save the Commissar.

209

He was ten metres from the embankment, when the burst from the Breda caught him full in the belly, where the itch had begun. He fell to his knees, gripping his belly. Theory bent down to him.

'On with the attack,' shouted Fearless, on his knees, holding onto his belly.

Galvanized by Fearless, the guerrillas crossed the open space and their grenades fell right in the enemy midst. Then the Commissar's group dared advance, Ekuikui among them. Ekuikui saw the Commissar, with his AK forgotten in his hands, staring at Fearless's countenance. Ekuikui touched him on the arm.

'Comrade Commissar, to the attack!'

'Go, advance, advance.'

And Joao ran towards Fearless.

The enemy no longer had any chance of flight on that flank. They retreated to the camp. The guerrillas pursued them. The Breda was silenced for ever.

Joao leaned over Fearless.

'Where are you hurt?'

'Child! Child, go and lead the assault.'

And he smiled at the Commissar. The latter squeezed him by the shoulder. He ran to the camp, shouting, but with tears in his eyes:

'MPLA advance! MPLA advance!'

His AK swept the ground. The soldiers tried to climb the hill, from which the mortars were already being withdrawn, and he aimed coldly, striking down the enemy, shot by shot. No-one bothered with camouflage. The guerrillas were firing, standing up and aiming carefully.

A few soldiers managed to escape the ring. Fallen Branch was taken.

The guerrillas recovered what they could carry: weapons and ammunition in the first place. Then they withdrew. The Commissar and Muatianvua carried the Commander to the rendezvous. Ekuikui took the motionless body of Struggle slung across his shoulders. On the way, the groups explained to each other the most significant factors in the battle.

At the rendezvous, they waited for the mortar group. Pangu-Akitina was trying to staunch Fearless's bleeding. Another guerrilla was wounded in the arm.

'Casualties?' Fearless asked in a whisper.

'One dead and two wounded,' the Commissar said.

'I saw Struggle fall. Is he dead?'

'Yes.'

'Struggle! Me likewise,' Fearless said.

'Not you.'

'I know I am. But, after all, I am not afraid of death . . .'

Pangu-Akitina packed all the dressings he had on Fearless's belly. The blood gushed out, it was impossible to staunch the haemorrhage. Pangu-Akitina's hands were soaked in blood.

'Useless,' the Commander said. 'Leave me here. I shall die in Mayombe. I shall not fight in Huila, it's a pity. Joao . . .'

'Yes.'

Fearless's voice was increasingly weak and the Commissar had to put his ear almost to the man's mouth to understand.

'Ondine cares for you. Try to win her back. You are made for each other.'

'Don't talk. Don't talk, it makes it worse. Does it hurt much?'

'It's bearable.'

Joao squeezed the Commander's hand.

'I beg for forgiveness, Fearless. I did not understand you, I was an imbecile. I wanted to match the unmatchable.'

Fearless shook his head.

'Gratuitous courage! . . . Just . . .' The Commissar did not respond.

After a few minutes Fearless gripped the other's hand.

'Joao.'

'What is it, Commander?'

'The mechanic, do you remember? The one we captured . . .'

'Yes.'

'He's in Dolisie . . . He came to join us . . .'

'I'll go and see him. Don't talk now . . .'

'Doesn't matter . . . Listen! The working class is joining the struggle . . . We are already winning . . .'

'Yes, Fearless. But don't talk, please.'

The Commander complied. He merely gripped the Commissar's

211

hand. The mortar group arrived. Everyone surrounded Fearless's body. It was then that firing began from the Sanga barracks. The tuga were directing mortars towards Fallen Branch. Sanga was not far away, the location was well known to the enemy, the mortars fell accurately on the camp.

The guerrillas were agitated.

'We must get out of here,' one said. 'They are aiming at Fallen Branch, because they think we're still there. Then they will aim further this way, next.'

'That would kill the Commander,' Pangu-Akitina said. 'He can't be moved from here.'

A light breeze arose and white specks from the flowers of the cotton-tree were falling gently.

'Snow in Mayombe?' Fearless asked.

The Commissar gripped his hand more tightly, in the desire to transmit to him the breath of life. But the life of Fearless was ebbing to the soil of Mayombe, and merging with the rotting leaves.

The shells now fell some two hundred metres from them. The guerrillas were complaining.

'No-one leaves here,' the Commissar shouted.

'Let them go, Joao. I shall stay . . . What better place to stay?'

But the Commissar did not hear what the Commander said. His lips now scarcely moved.

A giant mulberry tree in front. The trunk is distinguished from the forest's syncretism, but if I let my eyes follow the trunk up, its foliage merges in the general foliage and is again part of the syncretism. Only the trunk is distinct, is individual. Such is Mayombe, the giants are such only in part, at the level of the trunk, the rest is lost in the mass. Such is man. Visual impressions are less clear and the predominantly green tint gradually shades the clarity of the giant mulberry's trunk. The green tints are more and more prominent, but, all of a sudden, the trunk of the mulberry asserts itself again, by struggling. Such is life.

And what is the mechanic's face doing there in the trunk of the mulberry? He smiles at me.

Fearless's eyes remained open, studying the already invisible trunk of the giant which had disappeared for ever in its green element.

The Commissar shook from the thud of a shell less than fifty metres away. The men were grumbling and showing signs of moving. The Commissar faced them, an AK in firing position, and with his eyes blazing.

'Don't you realize that he's dead? He's dead! Fearless is dead! Don't you realize he's dead? Fearless is dead!'

The men looked at Fearless's expression and saw a smile on his lips. Was he smiling at life or at death?

'Let's go then,' Muatianvua said.

'Are you saying that we should go?' the Commissar shouted. 'You, of whom he was so fond? You, Muatianvua? No-one is going. We shall bury him here.'

'It's madness,' Ekuikui said. 'We don't have spades or picks. The shells are falling right by. Let's take him somewhere else.'

'We can dig with our knives, with our hands, with whatever you like. But he will be buried here. No-one has the right to carry Fearless dead. Where he died is where he will be buried. It is the only homage we can pay him.'

The Commissar threw himself on his knees, beside Fearless, and his knife bit madly into the soil. He was digging frantically, in time with his sobs. One by one, the guerrillas knelt beside him and copied him. The shells were now falling further off, at a diminishing rate. The men dug quickly, electrified by the Commissar, who was disappearing into the hole he was enlarging.

They put the bodies of the Commander and of Struggle in the hole and covered them. The Commissar did not speak, as was his right. There would be no funeral oration. Ekuikui was weeping silently. Truth too.

The Operations Chief said:

'Struggle, who was Cabinda, died to save a Kimbundu. Fearless, who was Kikongo, died to save a Kimbundu. It is a great lesson for us, comrades.'

Miracle, the bazooka-man, sighed and said:

'He was a great Commander! And Struggle a good fighter!'

He withdrew a few steps from the others and fired a bazooka missile which exploded in the trunk of a mulberry tree, some hundred metres from them. The guerrillas copied him and the AKs and Pepeshas sang out, in a last salute.

213

The flowers of the cotton-tree fell gently on the grave, and mingled with the green leaves from the trees. Within days, the place would be unrecognizable. The Mayombe would recover what men had dared to take from it.

EPILOGUE

I, THE POLITICAL COMMISSAR, AM THE NARRATOR.

The death of Fearless meant for me a change in the skin of twenty-five years, a metamorphosis. Sad, like any metamorphosis. I only understood what I had lost (perhaps my reflection projected ten years forward), when the inevitable occurred.

Fearless settled his basic problem: to maintain his own self, he had to remain there in Mayombe. Was he born too early or too late? In any case, he was out of time, like any tragic hero.

I evolved and I developed a new skin. There are some who need to write to shed the skin that no longer fits. Others change country. Others a lover. Others a name or a hairstyle. I lost a friend.

From the depths of Bie, a thousand kilometres from Mayombe, after a month's marching surrounded by new friends, where I came to take the place that he had not filled, I contemplated the past and the future. And I see how ludicrous is the existence of an individual. However, it is what marks the passage of time.

I think, like he did, that the frontier between truth and lies is a trick in the desert. Men are divided on the two sides of the frontier. How many are there who know how to find this sandy path through the midst of sand? They exist, however, and I am one of them.

Fearless knew as well. But he insisted that it was a track in the desert. So he laughed at those who said it was a path, cutting clearly through the green of Mayombe. Today I know there are no yellow tracks in the midst of green.

Such is the fate of Ogun, the African Prometheus.

DOLISIE, 1971

215

JUNE 22ND 2002

MAYOMBE IS A FINE BOOK.
NOT ONE I WOULD RECCOMEND
TO EVERYONE, BUT FOR THOSE
INTERESTED IN GURRILLA WARFARE
OR IN COLONIAL ANGOLA
IT IS A GOOD READ.
WEIRD, LIKE YAKA, AND
THAT MAY COME IN PART
AT LEAST DUE TO TRANSLATION

— Noah

August 12, 2008

A second time Through. Not a great book.
Perhaps some of that is the translation.
Seems To be the memoir of war
with some hero worship, or egoism.
Probabley not worth a third read.

Noah